LESLIE HALLIWELL'S
GREAT MOVIE CHALLENGE

LESLIE HALLIWELL'S GREAT MOVIE CHALLENGE

ARROW BOOKS

Arrow Books Limited
62–65 Chandos Place, London WC2N 4NW

An imprint of Century Hutchinson Limited

London Melbourne Sydney Auckland
Johannesburg and agencies throughout
the world

First published in 1989 by Arrow Books Limited

Phototypeset by Input Typesetting Ltd, London
Made and printed in Great Britain by
The Guernsey Press Co. Ltd., Guernsey, Channel Islands.

ISBN 0 09962020 0

Foreword

If you can give the correct answers to approximately two-thirds of the questions in this book, pray count yourself a Film Buff, First Class. That's roughly one thousand out of over fifteen hundred, and we give you an extra hundred questions in the Orientation Quiz as a starting bonus. More than 750 correct answers makes you a Second Class Buff, and with more than five hundred you can claim apprentice status. To make scoring easier, after each question there is a blank square to tick if you were right. Award yourself one point for each correct answer. And to guide you further, each separate subject is approximately graded as to difficulty, though even 'EASY' assumes a long-standing interest in the cinema.

There is a tendency to class all quizzes as trivia, but every scrap of knowledge about what has been achieved on our planet must be valuable in its way, and film has long been accepted as the key art of the twentieth century. Millions have ordered their lives by what they have learned at the cinema, and subsequent generations are learning through television what they may have missed the first time round.

However, I refer in this book chiefly to what has been classed as Hollywood's golden age, i.e. the first quarter-century of talkies, say from 1930 to 1955. Questions about earlier and later films do creep in, but few people now can have vivid personal recollections of the whole of the silent period, while most films of the seventies and eighties have appealed not to the whole audience but to young sensation-seekers who are content to see them in the dreary shoeboxes which have replaced the scented cathedrals of old. Most films are now seen at home, and *going* to the pictures is a pastime enjoyed by only a fraction of the crowds who once flocked to see Clark Gable and Bette Davis. So only a limited number of readers would be able to answer questions on the films of Jill Clayburgh or Gene Hackman; whereas Britain's Channel Four, which specializes in movies of older vintage, attracts with them enthusiastic audiences of up to six million, and has to fend off members of the still-burgeoning fan clubs for Al Jolson, Deanna Durbin and even Frank Randle.

5

So this book is undeniably bathed in that nostalgic orange glow which represents the past for modern film-makers, and which may well be the tint in which *The Maltese Falcon* is offered to future generations. (All we ask is that they leave the negative alone!)

On with the scoring!

Leslie Halliwell
Suffolk 1988

Questions

Orientation Quiz

1–2. Who were 'America's favourite lovebirds'?

3–4. In the Blondie films, what was Baby Dumpling's actual first name, and who played him?

5–6. Give two other release titles for the 1941 film sometimes known as *Daniel and the Devil*.

7–9. Humphrey Bogart and Lauren Bacall were scheduled in 1957 to make a film of John P. Marquand's *Melville Goodwin USA*. Bogart died, and Bacall withdrew. What was the title of the restyled film, and which two lead players appeared in it?

10. What American brothers were called Max and Buddy?

11–14. Who in show business was associated with Joice Heth, Chang and Eng, and the Wild Man of Borneo? And who played him in what two movies?

15–18. Two acting brothers and a sister changed their real surname, Blythe, to something more resonant. What was it, and specify all three.

19–22. What western outlaw was played, in what films, by Howard Duff in 1949, Nestor Paiva in 1946, and William Bishop in 1951?

23. What role did Adam West in 1965 take over from Lewis Wilson in 1943 and Robert Lowery in 1949?

24–8. What bandleaders used these theme songs? 'Babalu'; 'Minnie the Moocher'; 'Thinking of You'; 'Moonlight Serenade'; 'Rhapsody in Blue'.

29. What cartoon character was inspired by Helen Kane, the singer of the late twenties?

30–31. What pair of songwriters were the subject of 1950's *Three Little Words*, and who played Helen Kane in that film?

32. What song did Walter Mitty (Danny Kaye version) have in connection with Mighty Joe Young?

33–4. Who was Edward Teach, and who played him in the film which bore his nickname in the title?

35. Who played *Blackbeard's Ghost*?

36. Who played Redbeard?

37–8. Who played *Bluebeard* in 1944? And in 1972?

39. Who played *Bluebeard's Eighth Wife*?

40. And what about *Yellowbeard*? Who played him?

41. What characters did Pamela Britton and Arthur Lake in 1954, and Patricia Harty and Will Hutchins in 1967, play on television?

42–3. And who played them in the feature film series made between 1938 and 1948?

44. Who were Slip, Sach, Whitey, Bobby, Chuck and Gabe?

45–6. Steve Brodie claimed to have jumped off the Brooklyn Bridge in 1886. Who played him in what 1933 film?

47. What character was played by Buster Crabbe in 1939 and Gil Gerard in 1978?

48–9. Bob Clampett created Bugs Bunny in 1934 after watching what actor eat a carrot in what film?

50–1. What fictional detective was featured in two 1948 films, *Thirteen Lead Soldiers* and *The Challenge*; and who played him?

52–4. Of what TV comedy series were Gunther Toody and Francis Muldoon the lead characters, and who played them?

55. Keye Luke played Charlie Chan's son in the feature film series; what had he to do with the 70s cartoon series, *Charlie Chan And The Chan Clan*?

56. What long-running film and TV character was created by O. Henry in a 1907 story called *The Caballero's Way*?

57. What TV character connects Thomas Mitchell, Bing Crosby and Peter Falk?

58–9. Whose only line in his third film was as follows? 'Hey,

Gramps, I'll have a chocolate malt, heavy on the chocolate, plenty of milk, four spoons of malt, two scoops of vanilla ice cream, one mixed with the rest and one floating.' Also name the film.

60–3. What historical character has been played, in what films, by Erich Von Stroheim, James Mason, and Christopher Plummer?

64. Who was first seen in a 1935 movie called *The Little Wise Hen*?

65. Who was first cast as Dracula in the 1931 production?

66. Who was originally cast as the Frankenstein monster in the 1931 production?

67–8. What character, on TV in 1964–65, was 157 years old and called Lily? And who played her?

69–75. Western lawman Wyatt Earp has been portrayed in many movies. Who played him in the following? *Law and Order* (1932); *Frontier Marshal* (1939); *My Darling Clementine* (1946); *Wichita* (1955); *Gunfight at the OK Corral* (1957); *Hour of the Gun* (1958); *Cheyenne Autumn* (1964).

76. What was 'The Eyes and Ears of the World'?

77. Who was the original author of the *Destry* and *Dr Kildare* books?

78. Who was 'The First Gentleman of the Screen'?

79. *Harper* was a film based on a book about a detective named Archer. Why was the name changed?

80–3. Who were the original 'stars' of Four Star Television?

84. What TV programme used as its introductory theme tune the 'Funeral March of a Marionette'?

85. What Indian chief, whose name translated as One Who Yawns and who was much characterized in western movies, died in 1909 at the age of 80?

86. Why was the computer in *2001: A Space Odyssey* called Hal?

87–90. Who appeared on screen as a man reading a book on a train, a photographer outside a courthouse, and a man missing a bus? In what films?

91. Who was known as 'The Thief of Bad Gags'?

92–3. Whose last line in movies, in what film, was as follows? 'Just head for that big star. It will take us home.'

94–5. What role in what film was played silently by Francis X Bushman in 1926 and with sound by Stephen Boyd in 1959?

96. What star of the twenties died in 1932 after appearing in such films as *Where The North Begins* and *Jaws of Steel*?

97–100. By what name was Gertrude Margarete Zelle, who died in 1917, better known? Who played her in 1931, 1964 and 1985?

(100 points: answers on pages 135–7.)

Mr Laurel
And Mr Hardy

101–2. The first twenty minutes of *A Chump at Oxford* were tacked on afterwards, in order to bring a featurette up to feature length. In the opening sketch the comedians play maid and butler at a swank dinner party. Who is their employer, and of what 1928 film is the sketch a reprise?

103. What is odd about Finlayson's credit for this film?

104. Which of the silents climaxes in a mud-slinging match on a golf course?

105. What plot ploy connects *Be Big* and *Sons of the Desert*?

106. What two-reeler culminates in the destruction of a long line of cars stuck in a traffic jam?

107. In 1929 they planned a film about a family picnic, to be called *A Perfect Day*. What happened?

108. What is the similarity between *Angora Love* (1929), *Laughing Gravy* (1931) and *The Chimp* (1933)?

109–10. In which shot are they Christmas tree salesmen, and whose home do they break up?

111. In *Beau Hunks* (1931), Ollie joins the Foreign Legion to forget a woman who has forsaken him. We see her picture several times, and at the end it is revealed that half the Legion has joined for her sake. Whose picture was used?

112. In what 1933 short has Stan married Miss Hardy and Ollie Miss Laurel?

113. In what film do they play barbers?

114. What is the connection between Laurel and Hardy and a Charlie Chase short of 1936 called *On The Wrong Trek*?

115. *Tit for Tat* (1933) is a direct sequel to what other short produced earlier that year?

116. In what film do they perform the eyesie-earsic-nosie routine?

117. In what film do they play their own twin brothers?

118. When Stan was not available, who joined Hardy in *Zenobia* in 1939?

119. What Laurel and Hardy feature has among its supporting cast Alan Hale, Sidney Toler and James Finlayson?

120. What Laurel and Hardy film features the song 'Honolulu Baby'?

(20 points: answers on pages 137–8.)

All Creatures
Great And Small

The following title characters were all animals. What animals?

121. Ishtar.

122. Rhubarb.

123. Big Red.

124. Perri.

125. Francis (be precise).

126. Zenobia.

127. Gentle Ben.

128. Flipper.

129. Matilda.

130. Laughing Gravy.

(10 points: answers on page 138.)

Mind Your Ps,
Never Mind The Qs

The answers to these questions all have a conspicuous P.

Can you name:

131. The English village in which Dr Doolittle lived?

132. The same doctor's llama with a head at both ends?

133. The adventurer for hire played by Richard Boone in *Have Gun Will Travel*?

134. The valet played by Cantinflas in *Around the World in Eighty Days*?

135. The amorous French skunk of Warner Brothers cartoons?

136. The witch-heroine's feline familiar in *Bell Book and Candle*?

137. James Bond's female adversary in *Goldfinger*?

138. The professional name adopted by comedian Harry Einstein in the thirties?

139. The ship which goes up in flames in *The Maltese Falcon*?

140. The dictionary definition of Elwood P. Dowd's invisible friend Harvey?

(10 points: answers on page 138.)

Early Days

In each case you are given three examples of an actor's or actress's apprentice work, sometimes well before they received star billing. All you have to do is name the performer.

141. *Young Man of Manhattan, Queen High, The Sap From Syracuse.*

142. *The Man Who Played God, Bolero, Menace.*

143. *Girls' Dormitory, Ladies in Love, Love is News.*

144. *Two Man Submarine, She's a Soldier Too, Nine Girls.*

145. *Murder Man, Rose Marie, Next Time We Love.*

146. *Up the River, Quick Millions, Six-Cylinder Love.*

147. *The Finger Points, The Secret Six, Laughing Sinners.*

148. *Bad Sister, Seed, Way Back Home.*

149. *Night Ride, A Lady to Love, The Widow from Chicago.*

150. *Music for Madame, Maid's Night Out, Blonde Cheat.*

(10 points: answers on pages 138–9.)

Slight Seconds

These players contrived to remain in the limelight, for a time at least, despite physical disabilities which might have been fatal to their careers. Name them from a trio of their films, and specify the disability in each case.

151–2. *Trouble in Paradise, The Dark Angel, Foreign Correspondent.*

153–4. *He Who Gets Slapped, Riptide, The Women.*

155–6. *The Kid Brother, Movie Crazy, Professor Beware.*

157–8. *The Silver Fleet, Henry V, The Red Shoes.*

159–160. *You Can't Take It With You, On Borrowed Time, Key Largo.*

161–2. *Pretty Boy Floyd, Pocketful of Miracles, The Great Race.*

163–4. *Idol of Paris, Saturday Island, Timeslip.*

165–6. *Small Town Idol, The Love Parade, Our Wife.*

167–8. *Random Harvest, Keep Your Powder Dry, The Sign of the Ram.*

169–70. *The Private Life of Henry VIII, The Adventures of Tartu, The Cure for Love.*

(20 points: answers on page 139.)

They're Either
Too Young Or Too Old

From a trio of films in which each appeared, identify the following leading men who found employment in Hollywood during World War II when most regular male stars were on active service. In very few cases were the options of the replacements taken up when the war ended, and their Hollywood careers rapidly declined. *Another point in each case* if you can name the studio which put the actor under contract.

171–2. *The Mad Ghoul, Christmas Holiday, Can't Help Singing.*

173–4. *Hellzapoppin, Son of Dracula, Can't Help Singing.*

175–6. *Kitty Foyle, All That Money Can Buy, Our Vines Have Tender Grapes.*

177–8. *The Mummy's Tomb, Dragon Seed, The Climax.*

179–80. *So Proudly We Hail, I Love a Soldier, The Well-Groomed Bride.*

181–2. *The Very Thought of You, God is My Co-Pilot, Her Kind of Man.*

183–4. *Stage Door Canteen, Home in Indiana, Winged Victory.*

185–6. *The Song of Bernadette, The Eve of St Mark, A Royal Scandal.*

187–8. *Now Voyager, In Our Time, Between Two Worlds.*

189–90. *Hostages, Frenchman's Creek, Incendiary Blonde.*

(20 points: answers on pages 139–40.)

Yanks At Oxford
(and elsewhere)

Who were the intrusive Americans in the following British films?

191. *I Live in Grosvenor Square* (1945: he romanced Anna Neagle).

192. *Land Without Music* (1936: he supplied comic relief).

193. *The Grass is Greener* (1960: he had an eye for Deborah Kerr).

194. *The Earl of Chicago* (1939: he inherited a title).

195. *The Man in the Mirror* (1936: he was on both sides).

196. *A Yank at Eton* (1942: he shocked Freddie Bartholomew).

197. *Highly Dangerous* (1950: he helped a suspected lady spy).

198. *The Maggie* (1953: he found the Scots exasperating).

199. *A Yank in the R.A.F.* (1941: he enjoyed Betty Grable's company).

200. *The Way to the Stars* (1945: he comforted Rosamund John).

(10 points: answers on page 140.)

Were There No British Gels Available?

Name the European actresses who made the following forays into British films.

201. Opposite Stewart Granger in *Woman Hater* (1948).

202. Alongside Yvonne Mitchell in *The Divided Heart* (1954).

203. Opposite Serge Reggiani in *Secret People* (1950).

204. With David Farrar in *Lost* (1955).

205. Opposite Michael Redgrave in *A Stolen Life* (1939).

206. With Jack Warner in *Against the Wind* (1947).

207. Opposite David Farrar in *Frieda* (1947).

208. Opposite Ralph Richardson in *The Fallen Idol* (1948).

209. Opposite Alex Guinness in *To Paris with Love* (1954).

210. Opposite Joseph Cotten in *The Third Man* (1949).

(10 points: answers on page 140.)

Actors Should Be Treated Like . . . Gold Dust

moderate

Alfred Hitchcock often had trouble with his actors. He hardly ever got the ones he originally wanted, and some wooden leading performances ensued. His choice of character players, however, was unerring. In each of the following groups, the actors came together for a particular Hitchcock film. Which one? To hinder you more than a little, the leading players are not included.

211. Gene Raymond, Jack Carson, Philip Merivale, Lucile Watson.

212. Percy Marmont, Edward Rigby, Basil Radford, Mary Clare, George Curzon.

213. Leo G. Carroll, Martin Landau, Josephine Hutchinson, Jessie Royce Landis.

214. Leo G. Carroll, Nigel Bruce, Florence Bates, Melville Cooper.

215. Leo G. Carroll, Pat Hitchcock, Norma Varden, Marion Lorne.

216. Leo G. Carroll, Rhonda Fleming, John Emery, Michael Chekov.

217. Alma Kruger, Otto Kruger, Alan Baxter, Norman Lloyd.

218. Karl Malden, Brian Aherne, O. E. Hasse, Dolly Haas.

219. Frank Vosper, Pierre Fresnay, Hugh Wakefield, Nova Pilbeam.

220. Mary Clare, Catherine Lacey, Philip Leaver, Linden Travers.

(10 points: answers on pages 140–1.)

People Of Character

Name the following significant characters in popular films.

221. Who brought music to the people of River City?

222. Give the surname of the sinister family in *The Old Dark House*; Roderick, Saul, Horace and Rebecca – what?

223. As Cary Grant and James Stewart agreed in *The Philadelphia Story*, 'No mean Machiavelli is smiling, cynical, — —' – Who?

224. In the same film, to whom did Katherine Hepburn refer as 'A prince among men'?

225. What was Walter Matthau's nickname in *The Fortune Cookie*?

226. In what film did Becky Hutton play Gertrude Kockenlocker?

227. In what film is the leading villain called J. Worthington Foulfellow?

228. In what film would you find gentlemen called Shelby Carpenter and Waldo Lydecker?

229. In a film called *Fuddy Duddy Buddy*, name the character who said, 'I don't care if he is a walrus, I like him'?

230. Who plays Lord Paddington in *A Chump at Oxford*?

(10 points: answers on page 141.)

Actors We Like

Name the films in which:

231. Brian Aherne played Grace Kelly's priest.

232. Cedric Hardwicke played Boris Karloff's lawyer.

233. Melvyn Douglas played Raymond Massey's friend.

234. Anthony Quayle played Henry Fonda's lawyer.

235. Sydney Greenstreet played Errol Flynn's general.

236. Harry Davenport played Cedric Hardwicke's king.

237. George Macready played Thomas Mitchell's priest.

238. Peter Lorre played Victor Francen's secretary.

239. Cecil Kellaway played Joan Fontaine's servant.

240. Steve Geray played George Macready's lavatory attendant.

(10 points: answers on page 141.)

Not So Leading Ladies

Most Hollywood films of the 'golden age' took care to give equal prominence to male and female leads, in the hope that the film concerned would have equal appeal for both sexes. However, the heroine's role, especially in action films, is often very limited and instantly forgettable, limited to a kiss, a few screams and a final clinch. Can you say who shared romantic scenes as follows?

241. In *The Command* (1954) with Guy Madison.

242. In *Under My Skin* (1949) with John Garfield.

243. In *Sealed Verdict* (1948) with Ray Milland.

244. In *Little Boy Lost* (1953) with Bing Crosby.

245. In *The Cat's Paw* (1936) with Harold Lloyd.

246. In *A Time To Live and a Time To Die* (1958) with John Gavin.

247. In *The Mummy's Hand* (1940) with Dick Foran.

248. In *The 39 Steps* (1960) with Kenneth More.

249. In *Romeo and Juliet* (1954) with Laurence Harvey.

250. In *French Without Tears* (1939) with Ray Milland.

251. In *Mirage* (1965) with Gregory Peck.

252. In *Blindfold* (1965) with Rock Hudson.

253. In *House of Cards* (1968) with George Peppard.

254. In *The Killing* (1956) with Sterling Hayden.

255. In *King Creole* (1958) with Elvis Presley.

256. In *Son of Frankenstein* (1939) with Basil Rathbone.

257. In *Bullitt* (1968) with Steve McQueen.

258. In *Force of Arms* (1951) with William Holden.

259. In *The Oklahoma Kid* (1939) with James Cagney.

260. In *Arsenic and Old Lace* (1944) with Cary Grant.

(20 points: answers on page 142.)

When They Were Bad
They Were Horrid

Who are the famous stars, and what are the mercifully obscure films which they or their fans would like to forget?

261–2. In 1955 he starred along with Jack Palance and Pier Angeli in this biblical extravaganza from a book by Thomas B. Costain.

263–4. In 1969 she starred with Michael Redgrave in this drama about a seedy Bayswater boarding-house, written and directed by Franklin Gollings.

265–6. In 1952 this celebrated actor was the foil for knockabout comedians in a low-budget burlesque of pirate films.

267–8. In 1960 this comic actor flexed his thespian muscles and played a dastardly villain out to ruin Richard Todd's chances.

269–70. For her previous film she had a deserved Academy Award nomination, but no plaudits were forthcoming for this 1952 train-set farce.

271–2. Able to choose her own roles, she was unwise in selecting this wispy 1978 whimsy about two children launching a hot-air balloon.

273–4. A best-selling author, he shouldn't have chosen to star as his own creation in this 1963 crime thriller.

275–6. He lacked the protective warmth of the big studio in this 1943 comedy-drama about a newspaperman who exposes corrupt local politicians.

277–8. Having started as MGM's 'girl next door', she was at a loss in this 1969 melodrama about an attempted drug murder.

279–80. A sensitive star actor from the mid-thirties on, he was all at sea in this 1969 production as an arrogant, exhibitionist film producer. (His long-suffering wife was played by Leslie Caron.)

(20 points: answers on pages 142–3.)

What's In A Name?

The following names have all appeared on movie credits over the last fifty years. In what capacity?

281. Yakima Canutt.

282. O. W. Jeeves.

283. Mahatma Kane Jeeves.

284. Yma Sumac.

285. Hugo Butler (aka Robert Rich).

286. Erich Wolfgang Korngold.

287. Dr Ernst Toch.

288. Van Nest Polglase.

289. Binkie Stuart.

290. Arch Oboler.

291. Virginia Van Upp.

292. Edward Van Sloan.

293. John Van Eyssen.

294. W. S. Van Dyke.

295. Bretaigne Windust.

296. Travis Banton.

297. Edward A. Blatt.

298. Peverell Marley.

299. Hermes Pan.

300. Mario Castelnuovo-Tedesco.

(20 points: answers on pages 143–4.)

The answers here are titles which have been used more than once, for very different purposes. The clues should enable you to provide them.

301. In 1946, this Sherlock Holmes episode had Patricia Morison as villain; in 1980, the title covered a sensational murder story.

302. In 1943, Don Ameche was redirected to the upper place by Laird Cregar; in 1978, Warren Beatty followed in the footsteps of Robert Montgomery.

303. In 1932, the title bore no relation to the plot of a W. C. Fields extravaganza; in 1939, Betty Grable was the star of a collegiate comedy.

304. In 1931, stowaways ran riot on a luxury liner; in 1951, a scientist rediscovered his lost youth.

305. In 1943, Loretta Young solved a murder in Greenwich Village; in 1958, Kenneth More was among those assisting at a real-life disaster.

306. In 1952, Laurence Olivier went from bad to worse for love; in 1976, a teenage girl gained revenge by telekinesis.

307. In 1952, William Holden smashed a crime syndicate; in 1977, a housewife went back to the ballet.

308. In 1944, Tom Walls watched over a doomed love affair; in 1970, Ray Milland was equally helpless.

309. In 1947, Barry Fitzgerald gambled away his daughter's money; in 1966, a frogman salvaged treasure off the Californian coast.

310. In 1936, Herbert Marshall found himself spying on the opposite side from his former sweetheart; in 1944, a nun helped grounded flyer Ray Milland escape from the Nazis.

(10 points: answers on page 144.)

Here are some incomplete film titles with principal casts and dates. What you have to do in each case is insert an American state; you have fifty-one to choose from.

311. *Bad Men of* ——; 1941; Dennis Morgan, Arthur Kennedy, Wayne Morris.

312. *Christmas in* ——; 1945; Barbara Stanwyck, Dennis Morgan, Sydney Greenstreet.

313. *The* —— *Trail*; 1959; Fred MacMurray, William Bishop, Nina Shipman.

314. —— *City*; 1940; Errol Flynn, Randolph Scott, Miriam Hopkins.

315. ——; 1940; Wallace Beery, Marjorie Main, Leo Carrillo.

316. *Home in* ——; 1944; Jeanne Crain, June Haver, Lon McCallister.

317. —— *Conquest*; 1952; Cornel Wilde, Teresa Wright, Alfonso Bedoya.

318. —— *Crude*; 1973; Faye Dunaway, George C. Scott, John Mills.

319. —— *Johnson*; 1943; Van Heflin, Ruth Hussey, Lionel Barrymore.

320. ——; 1946; Ray Milland, Barbara Stanwyck, Barry Fitzgerald.

(10 points; answers on page 144.)

Occupational Hazards

Here are ten films whose titles explain, more or less, the occupations of their leading characters. Who played the title role in each case?

321. *Torch Singer* (1933).

322. *Taxi Driver* (1976).

323. *Taxi Dancer* (1926).

324. *Housewife* (1934).

325. *Housemaster* (1938).

326. *Society Lawyer* (1939).

327. *Night Nurse* (1930).

328. *Underwater Warrior* (1938).

329. *Downhill Racer* (1969).

330. *Six Day Bike Rider* (1934).

(10 points: answers on page 145.)

The Not-So-Swinging Seventies

Nobody in the film business is immune from disaster. What bottom-grossing films are described here?

331. 1974: Robert Ellis Miller directed this alleged comedy about an American correspondent in Moscow who falls for a Russian girl. Goldie Hawn, Hal Holbrook and Anthony Hopkins starred in it.

332. 1978: Once a master of disaster spectaculars (for instance *The Towering Inferno*), Irwin Allen came a cropper when he produced and directed this risible barnstormer. You might almost say he committed insecticide. Michael Caine, Fred MacMurray and Richard Chamberlain were among those involved.

333. 1976: Rod Steiger, Valerie Perrine and Jack Cassidy (as John Barrymore) starred in this woebegone and unhistorical attempt to explain the life of a famous comedian. Arthur Hiller directed.

334. 1970: Bud Cort, Sally Kellerman and William Windom were among those who took Robert Altman's direction in this airy-fairy fable about a young man who thought he could fly.

335. 1978: Robert Mitchum and Elliott Gould were among those involved in this sorry saga about a down-at-heel theatrical agent who finds success with a boxing kangaroo.

336. 1978: Peter Falk was expected to bring echoes of Bogart to this lame spoof of better movies including *The Big Sleep*, *Casablanca* and *The Maltese Falcon*. It was offered as a sort of follow-up to *Murder by Death*, which wasn't too good on its own account.

337. 1978: well into her eighties, Mae West was only an embarrassment in this raunchy version of a play she wrote for herself as a much younger woman. Tony Curtis and Ringo Starr were among those involved.

338. 1977: Wild Bill Hickok and Chief Crazy Horse joined forces

in this one to track down the semi-mythical beast of the title, a kind of north-western Moby Dick. Charles Bronson in the cast provided insufficient attraction.

339. 1976: a metropolitan apartment house turned out to be the gateway to hell in this Michael Winner shocker with Cristina Raines as its much-troubled heroine.

340. 1976: a troubled boy aims to castrate his mother's lover in this weird adaptation from the Japanese, set of all places in Dartmouth. Sarah Miles and Kris Kristofferson were involved.

(10 points: answers on pages 145–6.)

What's My Line?

Insert the correct profession or calling in each film title:

341. *The —— Was Indiscreet*

342. *The Nutty ——*

343. *Two Girls and a ——*

344. *The ——'s Daughter*

345. *The ——'s Paradise*

346. *Her Highness and the ——*

347. *The ——'s Candlesticks*

348. *——'s Pet*

349. *—— Story*

350. *—— Hardy's Children*

(10 points: answers on page 146.)

Mixed Doubles

These questions are about film titles with '*and*' in the middle, linking two names which are the principal characters in the story, as in *Bonnie and Clyde*. Name the two leading players (as titled) as well as the film. The clues given are the date and a synopsis.

351–3. 1980: in 1893, two girls head West in search of adventure.

354–6. 1942: a girl dresses as a child in order to travel half-fare on a train.

357–9. 1945: a cantankerous old man is tamed by his new housekeeper.

360–62. 1935: to prove her husband innocent of spying, a woman takes his place in Marlborough's army.

363–5. 1976: two famous Hollywood stars of the thirties get married.

366–8. 1947: an impressionable teenage girl has a crush on a headline-hitting playboy.

369–71. 1974: an escaped bank robber picks up with a young drifter.

372–4. 1947: a Quaker girl converts a gunslinger.

375–7. 1976: a famous comedian's mistress stays loyal.

378–80. 1976: an old cowboy falls for a young prostitute.

(30 points: answers on pages 146–7.)

Dignity,
Always Dignity

Here are ten words, each of which boasts at least three syllables. This fact alone would make these words unlikely candidates for film titles, but in each case we have in mind a film which used them as part of a longer title; your job is to guess it. Clues given are the production year and names of *two* of the supporting players: you have to name not only the film title but the male and female leads.

381–3. *History*; 1937; Colin Clive, Leo Carrillo.

384–6. *Century*; 1934; Roscoe Karns, Walter Connolly.

387–9. *Reformer*; 1950; Cecil Kellaway, David Wayne.

390–92. *Reincarnation*; 1974; Margot Kidder, Cornelia Sharpe.

393–5. *Imperial*; 1939; Reginald Owen, Gene Lockhart.

396–8. *Majesty*; 1954; Andre Morell, Abraham Sofaer.

399–401. *Impossible*; 1968; Chad Everett, Ollie Nelson.

402–4. *Covenant*; 1966; Earl Holliman, Sidney Blackmer.

405–7. *Horizontal*; 1962; Jim Backus, Miyoshi Umeki.

408–10. *Notorious*; 1962; Fred Astaire, Lionel Jeffries.

(30 points: answers on page 147.)

The answer in each case is a film which includes in its title the name of a country. (Sometimes the name of the country is the entire title.) Name each film with the help of its date and principal cast members.

411. 1953: Ray Milland, Arlene Dahl, Wendell Corey.

412. 1945: George Sanders, Virginia Bruce, Gene Lockhart.

413. 1947: Dick Haymes, Vera-Ellen, Celeste Holm.

414. 1954: Van Heflin, Howard Duff, Ruth Roman.

415. 1950: Tyrone Power, Micheline Presle, Tom Ewell.

416. 1944: Robert Taylor, Susan Peters, John Hodiak.

417. 1951: Rhonda Fleming, Mark Stevens, Nancy Guild.

418. 1983: Tom Selleck, Bess Armstrong, Jack Weston.

419. 1942: Preston Foster, Lynn Bari, Noel Madison.

420. 1945: Dorothy Lamour, Arturo de Cordova, Patric Knowles.

(10 points: answers on pages 147–8.)

Name the fictional crime-solving protagonist in each of the following movies.

421. *The Maltese Falcon.*

422. *The Big Sleep.*

423. *The Kennel Murder Case.*

424. *Kiss Me Deadly.*

425. *The Man on the Eiffel Tower.*

426. *The Alphabet Murders.*

427. *The Mirror Crack'd.*

428. *The Thin Man.*

429. *A Shot in the Dark.*

430. *The Case of the Howling Dog.*

(10 points: answers on page 148.)

A Rose By
Any Other Name

Movie titles get wilder. They thought so in 1933 when they heard about *Gabriel Over the White House* and in 1957 when *I Was a Teenage Werewolf* was premièred – and especially in 1966, when they sat still to watch the world's longest title unfold: *The Persecution and Assassination of Jean-Paul Marat as Performed by the Inmates of the Asylum of Charenton under the Direction of the Marquis de Sade*.

In 1987, which witnessed the premières of *The Belly of an Architect* and *Sammy and Rosie Get Laid*, one should perhaps be surprised at nothing. But are all the following genuine completed, reviewed cinema movies, as noted in the columns of *Variety*? Say true or false in each case, bearing in mind that many completed films do not get released.

431. *Diary of a Mad Old Man*, with Ralph Michael.

432. *All Passion Nearly Spent*, with Wendy Hiller.

433. *Kill!* with Arnold Schwarzenegger.

434. *Fat Guy Goes Nutzoid*, with Tibor Feldman.

435. *Amazing Grace and Chuck*, with Jamie Lee Curtis.

436. *Revenge of the Nerds II: Nerds in Paradise*, with Robert Carradine.

437. *The Garbage Pail Kids Movie*, with Anthony Newley.

438. *Allan Quartermain and the Lost City of Gold*, with Richard Chamberlain.

439. *Attack of the Killer Radishes*, with Aldo Ray.

440. *House II: The Second Story*, with Jonathan Stark.

(10 points: answers on page 148.)

The Bad And The Ugly

Playing a monster did no harm to Boris Karloff; it even revealed his fine acting talent. Nor could Bela Lugosi complain about the career which followed his impersonation of Count Dracula. Some of the monster impersonations below, however, were ill-advised. Can you name the actor involved in each case?

441. *Curse of the Werewolf* (1961).

442. *The Mummy's Hand* (1940).

443. *The Mummy's Tomb* (1942).

444. *The Return of Dracula* (1958).

445. *Man Made Monster* (1940).

446. *The Creature from the Black Lagoon* (1956).

447. *The Thing* (1952).

448. *The Undying Monster* (1943).

449. *The Invisible Man Returns* (1939).

450. *Werewolf of London* (1935).

(10 points: answers on pages 148–9.)

There's Always
A First Time

What stars made their first recorded talking film appearances as follows?

451. *This is the Night* (1932).

452. *Fighter Squadron* (1948).

453. *The Last Days of Dolwyn* (1948).

454. *The Maltese Falcon* (1941).

455. *The Strange Love of Martha Ivers* (1946).

456. *Service de Luxe* (1938).

457. *The Silver Chalice* (1954).

458. *The Kentuckian* (1955).

459. *The Way to the Stars* (1945).

460. *Dancing Lady* (1933).

(10 points: answers on page 149.)

Who played:

461. Noel Coward in *Star!*?

462. Sigmund Freud in *The Seven Per Cent Solution*?

463. Sigmund Freud in *Lovesick*?

464. Florenz Ziegfeld in *Funny Girl*?

465. Woodrow Wilson in *Wilson*?

466. Charles Lindbergh in *The Spirit of St Louis*?

467. Winston Churchill in *Young Winston*?

468. Field Marshal Douglas Haig in *Oh What a Lovely War*?

469. Jerome Kern in *Till the Clouds Roll By*?

470. Wernher von Braun in *I Aim at the Stars*?

(10 points: answers on pages 149–50.)

The Previous
Time Around

Irving Thalberg used to say that films are not made, but remade; he was referring to the cutting bench, but it's probably true that most movies owe a debt to a predecessor, and that debt is not always acknowledged. Here are 20 films, with the actors who played principal roles in them. Can you say of which previous movies they are unofficial remakes, and who played the roles in the first versions?

471–2. *Sergeants Three*: Sammy Davis Jnr.

473–4. *Broken Lance*: Spencer Tracy.

475–6. *The Fiend Who Walked the West*: Robert Evans.

477–8. *Barricade*: Raymond Massey.

479–80. *The Unfaithful*: Ann Sheridan.

481–2. *I'd Rather Be Rich*: Maurice Chevalier.

483–4. *Toy Tiger*: Jeff Chandler.

485–6. *Down and Out in Beverly Hills*: Nick Nolte.

487–8. *Maisie*: Ann Sothern.

489–90. *Once You Kiss a Stranger*: Carol Lynley.

491–2. *Lure of the Wilderness*: Walter Brennan.

493–4. *Treasure of the Golden Condor*: Cornel Wilde.

495–6. *Walk, Don't Run*: Cary Grant.

497–8. *Sincerely Yours*: Liberace.

499–500. *The Man Who Could Cheat Death*: Anton Diffring.

501–2. *In the Good Old Summertime*: Judy Garland.

503–4. *An Affair to Remember*: Deborah Kerr.

505–6. *Up in Arms*: Danny Kaye.

507–8. *The Shakiest Gun in the West*: Don Knotts.

509–10. *Fancy Pants*: Bob Hope.

(40 points: answers on page 150.)

Run For Your Life

Heroes of adventure thrillers are often in twofold danger: from the police who believe them guilty of murder, and from the villains because they know too much. What actor found himself in this unenviable position in the following films?

511. *The Clouded Yellow.*

512. *Three Days of the Condor.*

513. *Saboteur.*

514. *The 39 Steps* (1960 version).

515. *Man on the Run.*

516. *Mirage.*

517. *The Prize.*

518. *The Great Lover.*

519. *Young and Innocent.*

520. (one for the distaff side) *Woman on the Run.*

(10 points: answers on pages 150–1.)

521–3. 1940. Norma Shearer is an American-born countess living in Germany in the late thirties. She helps a young American (Robert Taylor) to find and rescue his mother, despite the fact that her lover (Conrad Veidt) is a Nazi colonel.
Name the film.
What silent star played the mother?
Who wrote the original novel?

524–6. 1941. Walter Pidgeon is a big-game hunter who purely for sport gets Hitler in his sights, and is ruthlessly hunted down by the Gestapo in the person of George Sanders.
Name the film.
And the director.
What was the title of the original novel by Geoffrey Household?

527–9. 1941. Bob Hope is a film star trapped by the selective service system, along with Lynne Overman, in a film with a punning title.
Name the film.
Give the female lead.
And the third member of the conscripted trio.

530–32. 1941. A surgeon experimenting in aviation medicine was the hero in this topical film, the chief pilots being Fred MacMurray and Regis Toomey.
Name the film.
Who played the surgeon?
And the female lead?

533–5. 1941. Tyrone Power, Betty Grable and John Sutton were the leads in this flag-waver with a title reminiscent of a 1938 film starring Robert Taylor.
Name the film.
The writer of the original story was also the producer and a top Hollywood mogul; name him.
What celebrated combined services action formed the climax of the story?

536–8. 1942. Thought to be in bad taste when it opened, this bitter comedy pokes fun at the Nazis occupying Poland and over the years has become a classic.
The film?
Who played 'Concentration Camp Erhardt'?
Who played Erhardt in the Mel Brooks remake forty years later?

539–41. 1942. In Britain this film opened as *Highway to Freedom*. It tells of a factory worker kidnapped and threatened by Nazi agents.
Give the original title.
Who played the hero?
How did he finally lead the FBI to the Nazis?

542–4. 1942. Hitchcock's American contribution to the war effort was a peripatetic thriller reminiscent of *The 39 Steps*. Robert Cummings and Priscilla Lane played the leads when he couldn't get Gary Cooper and Barbara Stanwyck.
Give the exact title of the film. (Careful.)
Where did the climax take place?
What actual disaster did Hitchcock slyly (and briefly) incorporate in the plot?

545–7. 1942. Dame May Whitty was the lady of the manor, Teresa Wright her daughter and Richard Ney the daughter's intended in this highly successful if unconvincing picture of the British in wartime.
Title, please?
What famous wartime action was incorporated in the story?
As a result of this film, what happened to Richard Ney in private life?

548–50. 1942. The stars would give it away, but can you name the film in which Marcel Dalio was the croupier, Leonid Kinskey the barman and Dooley Wilson the pianist?
Name the unpublished play on which it was based. (The title is used in the dialogue.)
Who was originally cast in the male lead?

551–3. 1943. *Hitler's Madman*, *Hangmen Also Die* and (thirty years later) *Operation Undercover* all stemmed their plots from the same actual event – which was what?

Name the British documentary reconstruction of the mass executions in Lidice which followed the assassination.

Several films were made similarly showing patriots being executed for resisting the Nazis; name the one in which Errol Flynn and Ann Sheridan, as Norwegians, were among the victims.

554–6. 1943. Claudette Colbert, Paulette Goddard and Veronica Lake starred as nurses in this Pacific War effort.
Name the film.
Which of the three heroines sacrifices herself and is blown up?
Name the producer/director, better known for Astaire – Rogers musicals a few years earlier.

557–9. 1943. Preston Foster, William Bendix and Lloyd Nolan were the leading actors in this recreation of a Pacific War battleground.
Name the film.
In the previous year which somewhat similar film starred Brian Donlevy, Robert Preston and Macdonald Carey?
And in 1949 John Wayne would star as Sergeant Stryker in which other film about an island held against the Japs?

560–2. 1944. Tallulah Bankhead, William Bendix and Walter Slezak were among those marooned by what director in an extremely confined acting space?
Name the film.
Name the 1949 film in which Hitchcock would also confine himself to one set for the entire film.

563–5. 1944. Robert Watson played Hitler, Martin Kosleck Goebbels and Victor Varconi Hess in this semi-documentary about how the Nazis gained power.
Name the film.
Watson became a celebrated Hitler impersonator, but in what Bob Hope film did he play the villain?
And in what film did he play a voice teacher entangled by two musical stars?

566–8. 1944. David O. Selznick's 'tribute to the American home' starred Claudette Colbert, Jennifer Jones and Shirley Temple.
Name the film.
Who played the husband who went away?
Who played the wartime lodger?

569–570. 1945. A major film of the war's end, about the problems facing returning servicemen, was based on a Mackinlay Cantor novel called *Glory For Me*, and in small roles were Gladys George and Ray Collins.
Name the film.
Harold Russell was the handless non-actor who collected two Academy Awards. Who played his girl?

(50 points: answers on pages 151–2.)

It Must Stand
For Something

Translate the initials in the following titles:

571. *D.O.A.*

572. *R.P.M.*

573. *O.S.S.*

574. *Z.P.G.*

575. *M*A*S*H.*

576. *The D.I.*

577. *S.N. A.F.U.*

578. *S.O.B.*

579. *G.I. Blues*

580. *F.P.I.*

(10 points: answers on page 152.)

An American town or city is missing from each of the following titles. Can you supply it, with the help of the date and principal cast?

581. —— *Cavalcade*; 1939; Alice Faye, Don Ameche, J. Edward Bromberg.

582. *The* —— *Story*; 1952; Jane Russell, Victor Mature, Vincent Price.

583. *The* —— *Story*; 1955; Edward Andrews, Richard Kiley, John McIntire.

584. —— *Rifle*; 1952; Gary Cooper, Phyllis Thaxter, David Brian.

585. —— *Speedway*; 1939; Pat O'Brien, Ann Sheridan, John Payne.

586. *The* —— *Story*; 1952; Joel McCrea, Yvonne de Carlo, Sidney Blackmer.

587. —— *Deadline*; 1949; Alan Ladd, Donna Reed, June Havoc.

588. —— *Exposé*; 1956; Lee J. Cobb, Patricia Medina, Edward Arnold.

589. *The* —— *Kid*; 1965; Steve McQueen, Edward G. Robinson; Ann-Margret.

590. *The* —— *Experiment*; 1984; Michael Pare, Nancy Allen, Eric Christmas.

(10 points: answers on pages 152–3.)

Catchphrase

What comic characters do you associate with the following exclamations? (There are five British, followed by five American.)

591. Don't be filthy!

592. What a performance!

593. You lucky people!

594. Get off me foot!

595. There'll never be another!

596. I have *nothing* to say.

597. Everybody wants to get into the act!

598. Godfrey Daniel!

599. I love that boy. Love him, I tell ya!

600. I don't care if he *is* a walrus. I like him. I like him!

(10 points: answers on page 153.)

Discoveries are sometimes better left undiscovered. In what films were these luminaries introduced to the international public, never to be seen again (except in a few cases in their country of origin)?

601. Diulio del Prete.

602. Klinton Spilsbury.

603. Jean Arless.

604. Neil Diamond.

605. Karen Lynn Gorney.

606. Ingrid Boulting.

607. Georges Guetary.

608. Katherine Houghton.

609. Patrice Munsel.

610. Jimmy Savo.

(10 points: answers on pages 153–4.)

One-Two Shots

The following performers were billed big and managed more than one film, but never fulfilled their promise. Name them from the data given.

611. She sang in the Vienna woods in *The Great Waltz* (1938).

612. He played Uncle Remus in *Song of the South* (1948).

613. Once known as Ted, he took another first name to be reintroduced in *The Unsuspected* (1948).

614. She was the author's alter ego in *A Certain Smile* (1958).

615. Darryl F. Zanuck gave her star status in *The Egyptian* (1954) and *The Racers* (1955).

616. He was cast as *The Public Enemy* (1930), but two days before shooting James Cagney was promoted to the role and he had to play the hero's friend.

617. She came from Finland, and went back there fairly fast after starring with Kenneth More in *The 39 Steps* (1960).

618. He starred in *The Adventurers* (1970), but it wasn't long before Yugoslavia called him back.

619. When she starred in *Algiers* (1938), the publicity boys said she came from the mysterious East, but it turned out they meant east of Manhattan.

620. He played the young hero – Elia Kazan's grandfather – in *America, America* (1963).

(10 points: answers on page 154.)

Laurence Olivier

Call him Sir Laurence, or Lord Olivier, or what you will – he has graced the world's screens on and off for more than half a century. Though he was never catnip at the box office and later in his career took on roles best left alone, his gallery of characters is magnificent. Name the following films from the data given:

621. In 1943 he played a Russian engineer perplexed by the British way of life.

622. In 1959 he played General Burgoyne in a semi-classic of the American Revolution.

623. In 1962 he played a schoolmaster falsely accused of rape by a pupil.

624. In 1938 he was a test pilot in an adventure film stolen by Ralph Richardson as a precursor of John Steed.

625. In 1931 he played a chauffeur to whom his mistress took a fancy.

626. In 1937, with Tamara Desni, he sampled a new discovery called a potato.

627. In 1935 (though the film was not released until 1940) he played Vincent Lunardi, an early balloonist.

628. In 1930, in a film made simultaneously in English and German (in the latter version Olivier's role was taken by Willy Fritsch), he played opposite Lilian Harvey as a woman on trial for the murder of her husband.

629. In 1935, in an English version of a French success, he played Ignatoff, a young Russian arrested as a spy.

630. In 1977, as Loren Hardeman Senior, he shocked many fans by participating in overt sex scenes in a screenplay generally considered fairly worthless.

(10 points: answers on pages 154–5.)

Very Important People

Some historical personages have been played by a great variety of actors, others by only one. Can you say in what film . . .

631. Simon Ward played Winston Churchill?

632. Greer Garson played Eleanor Roosevelt?

633. David Niven played Aaron Burr?

634. Basil Rathbone played Louis XI of France?

635. Harry Davenport played Louis XI of France?

636. Cedric Hardwicke played Charles II?

637. Alec Guinness played Charles I?

638. Cedric Hardwicke played Henry Cabot Lodge?

639. Laurence Olivier played the Duke of Wellington?

640. Orson Welles played Clarence Darrow?

641. John Mills played William Wilberforce?

642. Robert Donat played Charles Stewart Parnell?

643. Kenneth More played Kaiser Wilhelm II?

644. James Stewart played Charles A. Lindbergh?

645. Fay Compton played Queen Victoria?

646. Richard Burton played Henry VIII?

647. Robert Shaw played Henry VIII?

648. Agnes Moorehead played Queen Elizabeth I?

649. Alec Guinness played Benjamin Disraeli?

650. Raymond Massey played Philip II of Spain?

(20 points: answers on page 155.)

Graham Greenery moderate

For a fairly intellectual writer, Mr Greene has been surprisingly
well – though not always accurately – covered by the cinema.
Conscientious film fans should have no trouble in answering the
following test paper:

651. Which 1945 film from a Graham Greene novel starred
Lauren Bacall as an English 'honourable' and had Katina
Paxinou and Peter Lorre in supporting roles?

652. A 1972 version of a 1930s Greene novel starred Michael
York, and had its locale changed from Sweden to Nazi
Germany. Name it.

653. What 1947 film from a Greene novel suffered a changed
ending, so that the heroine kept her illusions about the criminal
hero?

654. After reading Graham Greene's film reviews, Alexander
Korda set him to work on the script of what turned out to be a
1940 co-feature starring John Mills, sometimes known as *Race
Gang*. What is its more usual title?

655. Another apprentice screenplay by Greene was adapted from
a Galsworthy story, 'The First and the Last'. Name the film,
which emerged in 1939.

656. A dog played a leading role in *Across the Bridge*, adapted in
1957 from one of Greene's stories. Who was the chief actor?

657. In 1956, Ken Annakin directed a rather frivolous Greene
script about love and money in Monte Carlo. For actors Greene
wanted Trevor Howard and Maggie Macnamara, but got
Rossano Brazzi and Glynis Johns. Name the film.

658. In 1957 James Cagney took his only shot at direction. The
film, *Short Cut to Hell*, was a remake of a 1942 production from
a Greene novel. Can you name, not the first film, but the
novel's original English title?

659. Greene absolutely hates a 1947 Technicolor film adapted by Muriel and Sydney Box from one of his movies. Which one?

660. The star of the last-mentioned film was unfortunate enough to appear ten years later in another Greene adaptation which the author disliked because of a changed ending. The co-star was Audie Murphy, the director Joseph L. Mankiewicz. Name the film.

(10 points: answers on pages 155–6.)

Hey, Mister!

The answers here are all movies with the word 'Mister' (or 'Mr')
in the title. The clue in each case is a synopsis, and the date of
production/release is added. Could we possibly be more helpful?

661. An eighteenth-century composer of German origin writes a
great English religious work (1942).

662. A middle-aged clerk joins the army and becomes a hero
(1944).

663. A Colorado melon-grower crosses swords with the local
Mafia (1974).

664. A surgeon is lured to an ex-girlfriend's remote home in
order to give her sadistic husband a new face (1961).

665. An amnesiac wakes up in Central Park and goes in search
of his identity (1966).

666. During World War II a gambling ship owner goes straight
and organizes Bundles for Britain (1943).

667. An exiled king in Hollywood meets a famous film star with
whom he once had a romance (1951).

668. A husband-and-wife dance team entertain the troops in
Japan (1951).

669. A San Francisco police lieutenant suspects a local minister
of murder (1970).

670. An elderly counterfeiter perplexes the US Treasury
Department (1950).

(10 points: answers on page 156.)

Brush Up
Your Shakespeare

671. What Shakespeare film was credited as having 'additional dialogue by Sam Taylor'?

672. What musical film was credited as being 'after a play by William Shakespeare – long, long after!'?

673. What Shakespeare play was turned into a modern gangster thriller starring Paul Douglas, Ruth Roman and Sid James?

674. Shakespeare's *The Tempest* was used in 1956 as the basis for what sci-fi fantasy?

675. What Shakespeare play was the basis for a melodrama about jazz musicians called *All Night Long*? (Patrick McGoohan starred.)

676. Akira Kurosawa's *Ran* is based on what Shakespeare tragedy?

677. And which tragedy was the basis for his *Throne of Blood*?

678. In 1959 the Danzigers (of all producers) used a Shakespeare play as the basis for a second feature board-room melodrama called *An Honourable Murder*. Which play?

679. What Shakespeare role do Edna May Oliver, Flora Robson and Pat Heywood have in common?

680. In what Shakespeare film can Arthur Treacher, Frank McHugh, Ross Alexander and Joe E. Brown be found among the cast?

(10 points: answers on pages 156–7.)

Frank Capra's People *moderate*

Frank Capra, born 1897, was a Sicilian who became an American folk hero and upholder – in his whimsical film fables and comedies – of the wisdom of the common people. In their day, and still on TV for those who can recapture the mood, these films stand near the peak of American cinema. How well do you know them?

681–3. A Robert Riskin script called *Platinum Blonde* (1931) concerned a newspaperman on a case; he falls for a society lady and neglects his fellow reporter Gallagher. Who played Gallagher?
Who (even more surprisingly) played the society lady?
And (even more difficult) what promising light actor won critical acclaim as the reporter hero, only to die of peritonitis before the film was released?

684–5. The rather dull hero of *The Bitter Tea of General Yen* (1933) was duller still in the same year in *The Mystery of the Wax Museum*. He played Lord Byron two years later in *The Bride of Frankenstein* and, after a fragmentary career, was the equivocal detective in the 1959 version of *The Bat*. Name him. Name too the Swedish actor who looked so uncomfortable as the oriental General Yen.

686–9. Apple Annie, the flower-selling heroine of *Lady For a Day* (1933), was played by an Australian actress who became a Hollywood fixture in a series of crusty granny and great-aunt roles. Name her.
When Capra remade the story in 1961, who played Apple Annie? Who was the butler? And what did he call the new version?

690–3. In *It Happened One Night* (1934) Claudette Colbert's rejected society suitor was played by a British actor whose success took him to Hollywood, though he made little headway there and died in 1939. Name him.
Who played Colbert's millionaire father? Who was the flirtatious bus passenger Oscar Shapeley? And what were the walls of Jericho?

694–5. Warner Baxter starred in *Broadway Bill* (1935), but who played the title role? And what was the title of the 1950 remake?

696–9. In *Mr Deeds Goes to Town* (1936), two character actresses played the Faulkner sisters. The first was Margaret McWade – who played the second? In court, they claimed that Mr Deeds was – what? Name the favourite Capra character actor who played the judge. And the other one who – without his usual moustache – was Mr Deeds' butler.

700–703. In *Lost Horizon* (1937) the novel's female character of an elderly British missionary was replaced by that of an American fast-liver now dying of TB. Who played the part? In James Hilton's novel, Conway and Mallinson were fellow diplomats; how did the Capra version intensify the relationship for dramatic purposes? Who played the leading female role of Sondra, which was not in the book? A. E. Anson and Henry B. Walthall were both considered for the High Lama, but both died before shooting began. Who did play the 200-year-old ascetic?

704–5. First billed in *Mr Smith Goes to Washington* (1939) is a character called Saunders. Who played the role? And who played the president of the Senate, on whose smile and shrug the film as it now stands fades out?

706–8. *Arsenic and Old Lace* was filmed in 1941 but not released until the play ended its Broadway run in 1944. The two old ladies around whom the play revolved cannot have been pleased to find themselves billed eighth and ninth. Who were they? Name also the actor who played mad brother Teddy; he went on to play Dockstatter in *The Jolson Story*.

709–10. *It's a Wonderful Life* (1946) was Capra's biggest disappointment. An American reworking of Dickens' Scrooge story, it proved despite its brilliance to be out of key with the post-war world, and only more recently has it been recognized as a classic. A key character is a little fellow named Clarence, who describes himself as – what? And who played the curmudgeonly Henry F. Potter, the tyrant of Bedford Falls?

(30 points: answers on page 157.)

Cherchez La Femme difficult

Although Hollywood's way was normally to give equal billing, very often the female star was of less box office importance than the male. Can you say who provided the romantic interest for:

711. Errol Flynn in *Rocky Mountain?*

712. Dana Andrews in *Berlin Correspondent?*

713. Cary Grant in *Once Upon a Time?*

714. Fredric March in *Tomorrow the World?*

715. Ronald Colman in *My Life with Caroline?*

716. Clark Gable in *But Not For Me?*

717. David Niven in *The Silken Affair?*

718. Cary Grant in *Arsenic and Old Lace?*

719. Humphrey Bogart in *The Big Shot?*

720. Stewart Granger in *Woman Hater?*

721. Elvis Presley in *Jailhouse Rock?*

722. Joel McCrea in *Foreign Correspondent?*

723. Richard Widmark in *The Last Wagon?*

724. Errol Flynn in *Montana?*

725. Humphrey Bogart in *In a Lonely Place?*

726. Gregory Peck in *The Omen?*

727. James Cagney in *The Oklahoma Kid?*

728. Bob Hope in *Monsieur Beaucaire?*

729. Gary Cooper in *The Westerner?*

730. William Holden in *Toward the Unknown?*

(20 points: answers on pages 157–8.)

Cherchez L'Homme

They do it with female stars too: one hesitates to count the number of times George Brent stood dutifully by Bette Davis, or Walter Pidgeon by Greer Garson. But who were the lesser-known male types squiring the ladies in the following cases? Who played opposite:

731. Bette Davis in *Winter Meeting*?

732. Barbara Stanwyck in *Lady of Burlesque*?

733. Merle Oberon in *This Love of Ours*?

734. Jennifer Jones in *Gone to Earth*?

735. Rita Hayworth in *Tonight and Every Night*?

736. Constance Bennett in *What Price Hollywood*?

737. Kim Novak in *The Amorous Adventures of Moll Flanders*?

738. Irene Dunn in *The White Cliffs of Dover*?

739. Joan Fontaine in *From This Day Forward*?

740. Ginger Rogers in *Fifth Avenue Girl*?

(10 points: answers on page 158.)

A.K.A.

Who played:

741. *Mister 880* in 1950?

742. *Santa Claus* in 1985?

743. *Windbag the Sailor* in 1936?

744. *The Mad Doctor* in 1940?

745. *The Mad Doctor of Market Street* in 1941?

746. *Our Girl Friday* in 1953?

747. *Our Man Flint* in 1965?

748. *The Madwoman of Chaillot* in 1969?

749. *The Gorgeous Hussy* in 1936?

750. *The French Lieutenant's Woman* in 1981?

751. *Old English* in 1930?

752. *The Man Who Changed His Mind* in 1936?

753. *The Man Who Could Work Miracles* in 1936?

754. *The Man Who Haunted Himself* in 1970?

755. *Johnny Come Lately* in 1943?

756. *Pygmalion* in 1938?

757. *The Greek Tycoon* in 1978?

758. *Salty O'Rourke* in 1944?

759. *Sorrowful Jones* in 1949?

760. *The Pride of the Yankees* in 1942?

(20 points: answers on pages 158–9.)

One movie per answer, the one which featured the given songs:

761. 'Could You Use Me'/'Embraceable You'/'I Got Rhythm'.

762. 'S'Wonderful'/'By Strauss'/'I Got Rhythm'.

763. 'I'll See You Again'/'Tokay'/'Ladies of the Town'.

764. 'Let's Knock Knees'/'Needle in a Haystack'/'Night and Day'.

765. 'Nice Work If You Can Get It'/'A Foggy Day'/'Stiff Upper Lip'.

766. 'That Look'/'Little Joe'/'See What the Boys in the Back Room Will Have'.

767. 'The Girl in the Police Gazette'/'This Year's Kisses'/'He Ain't Got Rhythm'.

768. 'I've a Strange New Rhythm in My Heart'/'In the Still of the Night'/'Who Knows'.

769. 'Pick Yourself Up'/'Bojangles of Harlem'/'A Fine Romance'.

770. 'Yesterdays'/'I'll Be Hard to Handle'/'Smoke Gets in Your Eyes'.

771. 'I'm Falling in Love with Someone'/'Tramp Tramp Tramp'/'Ah, Sweet Mystery of Life'.

772. 'Totem Tom Tom'/'Indian Love Call'/'Just for You'.

773. 'Mack the Black'/'Nina'/'Be a Clown'.

774. 'Varsity Drag'/'Pass that Peace Pipe'/'Lucky in Love'.

775. 'Old Man River'/'Cleopatterer'/'They Didn't Believe Me'.

776. 'Putting on the Ritz'/'A Couple of Song and Dance Men'/'Heat Wave'.

777. 'Meet Captain Custard'/'Sweet Potato Piper'/'Too Romantic'.

778. 'Lover, Come Back to Me'/'Softly, as in the Morning Sunrise'/'Stouthearted Men'.

779. 'Shuffle off to Buffalo'/'Young and Healthy'/'You're Getting to be a Habit with Me'.

780. 'When You Wish Upon a Star'/'An Actor's Life for Me'/'Give a Little Whistle'.

781. 'I've Got a Pocketful of Dreams'/'Small Fry'/'Don't Let That Get Away'.

782. 'They All Laughed'/'Let's Call the Whole Thing Off'/'Slap That Bass'.

783. 'I Used to be Colour Blind'/'Change Partners'/'The Yam'.

784. 'I'm Putting All My Eggs in One Basket'/'Let Yourself Go'/'Let's Face the Music and Dance'.

785. 'No Strings'/'Isn't This a Lovely Day'/'The Piccolino'.

786. 'Watch the Birdie'/'You Were There'/'What Kind of Love is This?'

787. 'Over There'/'Mary's a Grand Old Name'/'45 Minutes from Broadway'.

788. 'On the Banks of the Wabash'/'Lisa Jane'/'I'se Your Honey'.

789. 'The Anniversary Song'/'Sitting on Top of the World'/'The Spaniard who Blighted My Life'.

790. 'All Through the Day'/'Up With the Lark'.

791. 'You're the Top'/'My Heart Belongs to Daddy'/'Let's Do It'.

792. 'The Babbitt and the Bromide'/'Limehouse Blues'/'Bring on the Beautiful Girls'.

793. 'The Atchison', 'Topeka and the Santa Fé'/'Wait and See'/'Swing Your Partner Round and Round'.

794. 'I'll Capture Your Heart Singing'/'I Can't Tell a Lie'/'You're Easy to Dance With'.

795. 'Moonlight Becomes You'/'Constantly'/'Ain't got a Dime to my Name'.

796. 'That Old Black Magic'/'Hit the Road to Dreamland'/'I'm Doing it for Defence'.

797. 'I'm Old Fashioned'/'Dearly Beloved'/'Wedding in the Spring'.

798. 'You'll Never Know'/'Ragtime Cowboy Joe'/'Doing the Grizzly Bear'.

799. 'It's a Grand Night for Singing'/'It Might as Well Be Spring'/'Isn't It Kinda Fun'.

800. 'The Trolley Song'/'The Boy Next Door'/'Have Yourself a Merry Little Christmas'.

801. 'Swinging on a Star'/'The Day After Forever'/'Tooralooraloora'.

802. 'Happiness is a Thing Called Joe'/'Life's Full of Consequence'/'L'il Black Sheep'.

803. 'It Had to Be You'/'They're Wearing 'Em Higher in Hawaii'/'Whoopee'.

804. 'Long Ago and Far Away'/'Make Way for Tomorrow'/'Put Me to the Test'.

805. 'A Lovely Way to Spend an Evening'/'The Music Stopped'/'I Couldn't Sleep a Wink Last Night'.

806. 'The Lady in the Tutti Frutti Hat'/'Polka Dot Polka'/'No Love, No Nothing'.

807. 'They're Either Too Young or Too Old'/'Riding for a Fall'/'Love Isn't Born, It's Made'.

808. 'A Couple of Swells'/'I Love a Piano'/'Snooky Ookums'.

809. 'Johnny One Note'/'Thou Swell'/'Slaughter on 10th Avenue'.

810. 'What Lola Wants'/'You Gotta Have Heart'/'Shoeless Jo from Hannibal Mo'.

811. 'Small Talk'/'Racing with the Clock'/'Hernando's Hideaway'.

812. 'My Funny Valentine'/'I Didn't Know What Time It Was'/'Bewitched, Bothered and Bewildered'.

813. 'Clap Your Hands'/'Bonjour Paris'/'Think Pink'.

814. 'I Whistle a Happy Tune'/'Hello, Young Lovers'/'Is Puzzlement'.

815. 'Now You Has Jazz'/'True Love'/'Swell Party'.

816. 'I Can't Say No'/'Poor Jud is Dead'/'People Will Say We're in Love'.

817. 'Stranger in Paradise'/'Gesticulate'/'Baubles, Bangles and Beads'.

818. 'Popo the Puppet'/'Happy Ending'/'Balling the Jack'.

819. 'Come Up to My Place'/'You're Awful'/'You Can Count on Me'.

820. 'Shoes with Wings On'/'My One and Only Highland Fling'/ 'They Can't Take That Away from Me'.

821. 'Moses Supposes'/'Fit as a Fiddle'/'Good Morning'.

822. 'O'Brien to Ryan to Goldberg'/'The Right Gal for Me'/'The Hat My Father Wore'.

823. 'Thumbelina'/'No Two People'/'The Ugly Duckling'.

824. 'The Hostess with the Mostest'/'You're Just in Love'/ 'International Rag'.

825. 'Wunderbar'/'Where is the Life That Late I Led?'/'Brush Up Your Shakespeare'.

826. 'I Love Louisa'/'A Shine on your Shoes'/'That's Entertainment'.

827. 'I'm an Indian Too'/'Who Do You Love, I Hope?'/'Doin' What Comes Naturally'.

828. 'Higher Than a Hawk'/'Just Blew In from the Windy City'/ 'I Can Do Without You'.

829. 'Man and Woman'/'Lady Killer'/'A Dime and a Dollar'.

830. 'Something's Gotta Give'/'The Slue Foot'/'How I Made the Team'.

831. 'Luck, Be a Lady'/'Sue Me'/'The Oldest Established'.

832. 'When You're in Love'/'Bless Your Beautiful Hide'/'Goin' Courtin''.

833. 'Almost Like Being in Love'/'The Heather on the Hill'/'I'll Go Home With Bonnie Jean'.

834. 'After You Get What You Want You Don't Want It'/'Play a Simple Melody'/'Alexander's Ragtime Band'.

835. 'I Like Myself'/'Baby You Knock Me Out'/'Thanks a Lot But No Thanks'.

836. 'The Sadder but Wiser Girl'/'Gary Indiana'/'Shipoopi'.

837. 'What Do the Simple Folk Do?'/'C'est Moi'/'How to Handle a Woman'.

838. 'If Mama Were Married'/'Let Me Entertain You'/'You Gotta Have a Gimmick'.

839. 'Let's Go Fly a Kite'/'Chim-Chim-Cheree'/'A Spoonful of Sugar'.

840. '16 Going On 17'/'Do Re Mi'/'So Long, Farewell'.

(80 points: answers on pages 159–61.)

City Of My Dreams

The answers here are all towns or cities which have served, alone and uncluttered by additional vocabulary, as film titles. We give you the principal cast and the date: please supply the titles.

841. 1958: Yvonne de Carlo, Victor Mature, George Dolenz.

842. 1938: Charles Boyer, Hedy Lamarr, Sigrid Gurie.

843. 1955: Richard Conte, Victor McLaglen, Richard Carlson.

844. 1956: Ray Milland, Claude Rains, Maureen O'Hara.

845. 1936: Clark Gable, Jeanette MacDonald, Spencer Tracy.

846. 1956: Errol Flynn, Cornell Borchers, John Bentley.

847. 1941: Jeanette MacDonald, Robert Young, Ethel Waters.

848. 1939: Basil Rathbone, Victor McLaglen, Sigrid Gurie.

849. 1963: George Sanders, Richard Johnson, Faten Hamama.

850. 1946: Alan Ladd, Gail Russell, William Bendix.

(10 points: answers on page 162.)

My Story

Who played the title role in the following biopics?

851. *The Eddy Duchin Story.*

852. *The Gene Krupa Story.*

853. *The Babe Ruth Story.*

854. *The George Raft Story.*

855. *The Buster Keaton Story.*

856. *The Buddy Holly Story.*

857. *The Eddie Cantor Story.*

858. *The Will Rogers Story.*

859. *The Grace Moore Story.*

860. *The Helen Morgan Story.*

861. *Beau James* (Jimmy Walker).

862. *Tennessee Johnson.*

863. *The Unsinkable Molly Brown.*

864. *Jeanne Eagels.*

865. *Melba.*

866. *The Iron Duke* (Wellington).

867. *The Prime Minister* (Disraeli).

868. *Lady Caroline Lamb.*

869. *Evel Knievel.*

870. *The Flying Irishman.*

(20 points: answers on pages 162–3.)

The Haunted House Of Hammer

For twenty years Hammer Studios filled our screens with a wild variety of supernatural malarkey. Can you name the actors who indulged in the following eccentric behaviour? Can you also name the films?

871–2. As Kallikrates, he played an immortal stalking the earth in search of his lost love Ayesha (1967).

873–4. As a Cornish squire, he created a band of the undead to work an old tin mine (1966).

875–6. As Ravna, he ran a vampire club which was destroyed by avenging bats (1964).

877–8. As Greta, by night she coaxed the recent dead from their newly-covered graves (1960).

879–80. As Carla, she turned into a fabulous Greek monster with hissing serpents in her head of hair (1964).

881–2. As 'Adam Beauchamp' he wearily travelled the world for 3000 years in the hope of being relieved of an ancient curse (1964).

883–4. As Anna Franklin, as the result of a curse placed on her by an obscure Malayan sect, she changed periodically into a snake-woman (1966).

885–6. As Georges Bonner, he needed periodic gland injections to conceal his real age of 104 and keep on looking 39 (1959).

887–8. As Professor Richter, he took revenge on Frankenstein for replacing his brain with that of a manic surgeon (1968).

889–90. As Mircalla Karnstein, she rose from the dead to claim young girls as her sexual victims (1970).

(20 points: answers on page 163.)

The Hammer Ladies *moderate*

Leading ladies in Hammer horror films tended to appear more in the daily tabloids than on screen, where their nubile charms were usually displayed only once before they returned to some exotic native habitat (Fulham, in one case at least). Can you say in which frightful flick each of the following was first waved before a dutifully impressed world?

891. Carita (as Salina).

892. Maggie Kimberley (as Claire).

893. Olinka Berova (as Carol).

894. Jeanne Roland (as Annette Dubois).

895. Yvonne Monlaur (as Marianne).

896. Susan Denberg (as Christina).

897. Veronica Carlson (as Maria).

898. Victoria Vetri (as Sanna).

899. Julie Ege (as Nala).

900. Martine Beswick (as Kari).

(10 points: answers on page 163.)

Black-Hearted Men

Who played, and in what films:

901–2. Auric Goldfinger in 1964?

903–4. Carver Doone in 1934?

905–6. Peter Quint in 1971?

907–8. Professor Moriarty in 1976?

909–10. The Sheriff of Nottingham in 1938?

911–12. Injun Joe in 1938?

913–14. Uriah Heep in 1935?

915–16. Bill Sikes in 1948?

917–18. Ralph Nickleby in 1947?

919–20. Sweeney Todd in 1936?

921–2. Count Fosco in 1948?

923–4. The Chevalier del Gardo in 1939?

925–6. Claude Frollo in 1939?

927–8. The Marquis de St Evremonde in 1935?

929–30. Robespierre in 1939?

931–2. Svengali in 1931?

933–4. Fu Manchu in 1932?

935–6. Black Michael in 1937?

937–8. Long John Silver in 1935?

939–40. The Marquis de Sade in 1969?

(40 points: answers on page 164.)

Celebrated stars and directors, plus one writer, reminisce about their films. Which films? The date given is the date of the reminiscence, so the film must predate that . . .

941. Joan Crawford in 1962: 'What worried George Cukor was my emotionalism. . . . He anticipated that wearing a scar could affect me as wearing a cape has been known to affect some actors . . . '

942. Howard Koch in 1973: 'With the deadline creeping up on me and with Mike Curtiz asking when he was going to get pages, a kind of paralysis came over me. . . . Finally, in desperation, I decided to forget there was no story-line and just start writing scenes as they came to me. . . . I had only the vaguest notion where each scene was leading, just hoping that it would lead to another scene, and that the sum total, if I lived that long, would add up to a film that wouldn't be bad enough to end my brief career in Hollywood . . . '

943. Henry Fonda in 1959: 'When I first agreed to do it, the script by Irwin Shaw was fine. But what happened? The director, King Vidor, used to go home at night with his wife and rewrite it. All the genius . . . went out of the window. Inevitably, it was a disaster.'

944. Rouben Mamoulian in 1961: 'Garbo asked me, "What do I play in this scene?" I said, "I want your face to be a blank sheet of paper. I want the writing to be done by every member of the audience. . . . " So in fact there is *nothing* on her face, but everyone who has seen the film will tell you what she is thinking and feeling, and always it's something different.'

945. Katharine Hepburn in 1974: 'Spencer and I wanted so much to make it. It was a great book. But it was loused up by being done on a sound stage instead of on location. We were both tremendously disappointed with it.'

946. James Cagney in 1959: 'I've just finished a picture . . . The closest thing to it, I'd say, was *The Threepenny Opera*. It's all

about a bunch of crooks who try to operate on big business lines. It's witty, and it has some good radical lyrics. Films must have some comment to make. They've got to keep moving.'

947. Frank Capra in 1972: 'We couldn't get a girl to play this thing. We offered the part to Miriam Hopkins, Myrna Loy, Connie Bennett, and Margaret Sullavan, and they all turned it down, and finally we got hold of (————— —————). She was on a four-week vacation and she liked money, being French.'

948. Alfred Hitchcock in 1968: 'I had the woman dressed in black to begin with, and then as the tragedy overtook her she went to brick, then to grey, then to black.'

949. Elia Kazan in 1974: '*Gentleman's Agreement* was such a big hit that Zanuck naturally said, "Let's do it again with a Negro." And this time he got Ford to direct it. Ford started it and shot about ten days. . . . '

950. Stanley Kramer in 1963: 'My first, and probably my last, epic. You know what happened on that one? Sinatra just jumped the picture a month before the end. He just took off. We never saw him again. (————— —————) had to do all his final close-ups talking to a clothes-hanger.'

(10 points: answers on pages 164–5.)

Not All My Own Work

What celebrated writers of our century worked for Hollywood studios, producing screenplays as follows from other people's originals?

951. *Five Came Back* (1939); *I Stole a Million* (1939).

952. *All Quiet on the Western Front* (1930); *Death Takes a Holiday* (1934).

953. *To Have and Have Not* (1945); *The Big Sleep* (1946).

954. *City Streets* (1931); *After the Thin Man* (1936).

955. *Pride and Prejudice* (1940); *Jane Eyre* (1944).

956. *Rage in Heaven* (1941); *The Loved One* (1965).

957. *Horse Feathers* (1932); *Around the World in 80 Days* (1956).

958. *And Now Tomorrow* (1944); *The Unseen* (1945).

959. *A Yank at Oxford* (1938) (uncredited); *Three Comrades* (1939).

960. *The Dark Angel* (1935); *The Case* (1966).

(10 points: answers on page 165.)

Name And Address

Name the principal male star of:

961. *13 West Street.*

962. *Ten North Frederick.*

963. *Scarlet Street.*

964. *26 Acacia Avenue.*

965. *13 Rue Madeleine.*

966. *711 Ocean Drive.*

967. *Quai des Orfèvres.*

968. *St Martin's Lane.*

969. *The House on Haunted Hill.*

970. *The House on the Square.*

(10 points: answers on page 165.)

The following section is based on press advertisements from which the title of the film concerned has been deleted. Your first task is to name it from the illustrations; there are then four other questions about the people involved.

971. Title?

972. What world-famous man did Jean Peters marry?

973. Jeffrey Hunter appeared as Christ in a 1961 film snidely known as *I Was a Teenage Jesus*. What was its official title?

974. In what film did Walter Brennan go around asking people 'Was you ever stung by a dead bee?'

975. Jean Negulesco directed not only *Three Coins in the Fountain*, set in Rome, but its 1964 remake set in Madrid. Name the remake.

IT'S A WILD-DAY!... IT'S A WACKY DAY...

HAROLD LLOYD in

THE MOST COMPLETELY BOLLIXED-UP DAY YOU EVER HEARD OF!
—JIMMY CONLIN RAYMOND WALBURN ARLINE JUDGE EDGAR KENNEDY FRANKLIN
PANGBORN LIONEL STANDER MARGARET HAMILTON ... —FRANCES RAMSDEN
Written, Directed and Produced by PRESTON STURGES

976. Title?

977. Name Harold Lloyd's previous film, made in 1938: he played an Egyptologist.

978. In what film did Raymond Walburn play Gary Cooper's butler?

979. In what film was Edgar Kennedy hired by Rex Harrison as a private detective?

980. In what film was Franklin Pangborn a film producer listening to a story told by W. C. Fields?

MEN WANTED

Private company with C.I.A. contract seeks men willing to risk life. Long career doubtful.

JAMES CAAN
ROBERT DUVALL

in A SAM PECKINPAH Film

An ARTHUR LEWIS – BAUM/DANTINE Production · co-starring ARTHUR HILL · BO HOPKINS MAKO · and GIG YOUNG · Directed by SAM PECKINPAH · Screenplay by MARC NORMAN and STIRLING SILLIPHANT · From the novel by ROBERT ROSTAND · Produced by MARTIN BAUM and ARTHUR LEWIS · Production Services by Double Dee Service Company · An EXETER/PERSKY-BRIGHT Feature

PG PARENTAL GUIDANCE SUGGESTED
SOME MATERIAL MAY NOT BE SUITABLE FOR PRE-TEENAGERS

United Artists

THEATRE

981. Title?

982. In what classic science-fiction film of 1956 did Sam Peckinpah play a small acting role?

983. In what 1975 film was James Caan directed by Karel Reisz?

984. What famous figure of World War 2 did Robert Duvall portray in a 1979 TV mini-series?

985. For what film did Gig Young receive an Academy Award?

81

WARNER BROS.'
WIDE-OPEN STORY
OF THE PRIVATE
LADY OF A PUBLIC
ENEMY!

*A Flaming New Screen
Sensation with the
'Flamingo Road Team!*

JOAN
CRAWFORD · DAVID
BRIAN

WITH STEVE COCHRAN
KENT SMITH

DIRECTED BY
VINCENT SHERMAN · JERRY WALD
PRODUCED BY

Screen play by Harold Medford and Jerome Weidman · Story by Gertrude Walker

986. Title?

987. For what film did Joan Crawford win an Academy Award?

988. In what film did David Brian help a small boy and an old lady discover the truth about a murder?

989. In what film did Steve Cochran play a member of the Ku-Klux-Klan?

990. Vincent Sherman directed Bette Davis in two films. Name one of them.

"Is it love or guilt that's making you marry me after all these years!"

THE TOWN MARSHAL...AND THE TOWN'S WOMAN...
TOGETHER THEY BROKE ALL THE RULES!

Richard Widmark
Lena Horne in

M

CO STARRING
Carroll O'Connor and **John Saxon** as LOU TRINIDAD

From the novel by LEWIS B. PATTEN Screenplay by JOSEPH CALVELLI
Directed by ALLEN SMITHEE · Produced by RICHARD E. LYONS

A UNIVERSAL PICTURE
TECHNICOLOR®

991. Title?

992. Richard Widmark made his name playing a criminal called Tommy Udo. In what film?

993. Among Lena Horne's first film appearances was an all-star all-black musical in which she partnered Bill Robinson in 1944. Name it.

994. Carroll O'Connor found his greatest fame as what loud-mouthed TV character?

995. What do you know about the director Allen Smithee?

996. Title?

997. Mitzi Gaynor was a hard worker who never quite reached superstardom, despite appearing in what mammoth Rodgers and Hammerstein film musical in 1958?

998. Keefe Brasselle's career continued in low key, especially after he impersonated what famous Broadway singer-comedian in a 1953 biopic?

999. Aaron Spelling figures among the supporting cast. His greatest claim to fame, however, was not as an actor but as ... what?

1000. Henry Levin's directorial career was not especially notable, but in 1959 he did carry off with aplomb a Hollywood version of what Jules Verne fantasy?

1001. Title?

1002. Edmund Lowe had a long and lucrative career in movies. With what actor was he often paired in comedy action films, after they played Flagg and Quirt in the 1926 version of *What Price Glory*?

1003. What was Mae West's first film, the one in which someone said, 'Goodness, what beautiful diamonds!' and she replied 'Goodness had nothing to do with it.'?

1004. Charles Winninger was an old Broadway trouper. In the 1941 *Ziegfeld Girl*, with whom did he perform a reminiscence of a famous double act?

1005. Walter Catlett also came from vaudeville. In what film was he a jailkeeper who locked up Katharine Hepburn?

85

SHE OUTLIVED SIX RICH MEN...
HE WAS A TAKER ALL HIS LIFE...

they do things you've never seen before!

Elizabeth Taylor
Richard Burton
Noel Coward

in a *John Heyman Production*
Joseph Losey's

by *Tennessee Williams*

Also starring **JOANNA SHIMKUS** MICHAEL DUNN
Music by JOHN BARRY • Screenplay by TENNESSEE WILLIAMS • Directed by JOSEPH LOSEY
Associate Producer LESTER PERSKY • Produced by JOHN HEYMAN and NORMAN PRIGGEN
A Universal Pictures Limited / World Film Services Limited Production **TECHNICOLOR • PANAVISION**

Suggested For Mature Audiences

1006. Title?

1007. In 1973 Elizabeth Taylor made a film which was barely released, from a novel by Iris Murdoch. Name it.

1008. Name Richard Burton's first film, in which he supported Dame Edith Evans.

1009. In Noel Coward's first American film, in 1935, he played a ghost. Name it.

1010. When Joseph Losey was blacklisted as a communist, he made a film in Britain under the pseudonym Walton (after the studios in which it was filmed). Name it.

86

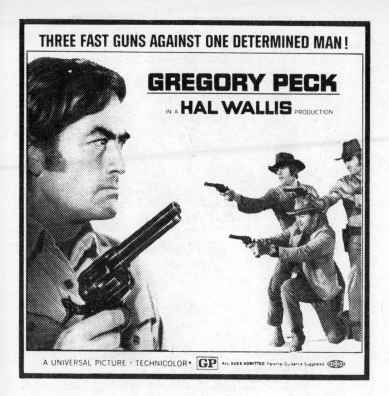

THREE FAST GUNS AGAINST ONE DETERMINED MAN!

GREGORY PECK
IN A **HAL WALLIS** PRODUCTION

A UNIVERSAL PICTURE · TECHNICOLOR® **GP** ALL AGES ADMITTED Parental Guidance Suggested

1011. Title?

1012. Name Gregory Peck's first film, which had a Russian setting and co-starred Tamara Toumanova.

1013. Hal Wallis was for many years the essential production boss at Warner Studios. Name the leading lady, co-star of *The Carpetbaggers*, whom he married in middle life.

1014. Henry Hathaway was known for his action pictures; but in 1935 he admirably handled a strange supernatural romance with Gary Cooper and Ann Harding, from a novel by George du Maurier. Name it.

1015. Gregory Peck almost always played good guys, but in which film did he play the rascally Lewt McCanles?

1016. Title?

1017. In what film did Robert Mitchum have 'LOVE' tattooed on the fingers of one hand, and 'HATE' on the other?

1018. Teresa Wright won an Academy Award for *Mrs Miniver*, but what was her previous (and first) film, in which she had a tempestuous final scene with Bette Davis?

1019. William Wellman was another action director, but please name his much quieter 1939 film starring Ronald Colman as a blind artist.

1020. In what film did Diana Lynn play Emily Kockenlocker?

**EIGHT PEOPLE KNOW
WHO THE KILLER IS.
AND THEY'RE ALL DEAD.**
Motive unknown. Killer unknown.

Every clue is cold.
Every lead is blind.
Every suspect
is dead.
When will
the killer
strike again...
and why are the
cops so scared?

A 20th Century-Fox Presentation

Walter Matthau and **Bruce Dern**
race against time and a killer in

Best Mystery Novel
of the Year.
— Mystery Writers of America

Co-starring Lou Gossett

Albert Paulsen · Anthony Zerbe · Directed and Produced by Stuart Rosenberg
Screenplay by Thomas Rickman · Based on the novel by Per Wahloo and Maj Sjowall

R RESTRICTED Music Charles Fox · COLOR BY DE LUXE ®

1021. Title?

1022. In what film did Walter Matthau play a sharp lawyer known
as Whiplash Willie?

1023. In one of Bruce Dern's first films he had his head and
hand cut off by a deranged murderer who may or may not
have been Bette Davis. Name the film.

1024. Lou Gossett, with or without the 'Jnr' which he sometimes
sports, won an Academy Award for his performance as a tough
serviceman in – what?

89

1025. Stuart Rosenberg's most acclaimed film included in its cast Strother Martin as a sadistic bully who uttered the words: 'What we have here is a failure to communicate.' Name the film.

HERE'S THAT MAN FROM "THE MOB"!

BLACKMAILERS!

SHOCK-SLAYERS!

Brod's back in a new racket —hawking heartbreak a nickel a look, a thrill, a secondhand shock!

LOVE NESTERS!

COLUMBIA PICTURES presents

BRODERICK CRAWFORD

DONNA REED · JOHN DEREK

with ROSEMARY DE CAMP · HENRY O'NEILL · HENRY MORGAN
Screen Play by TED SHERDEMAN, EUGENE LING and JAMES POE · Produced by EDWARD SMALL · Directed by PHIL KARLSON

1026. Title?

1027. For what previous film did Broderick Crawford win an Academy Award?

1028. Name the comedienne who appeared with Fred Astaire and Ginger Rogers in *Top Hat* and was Broderick Crawford's mother.

1029. For what film did Donna Reed receive an Academy Award?

1030. In what 1950 film did John Derek play Robin Hood?

20th CENTURY-FOX PRESENTS A BERNSEN-LUDWIG-BERCOVICI PRODUCTION

JIM BROWN   LEE VAN CLEEF
FRED WILLIAMSON   CATHERINE SPAAK
JIM KELLY   BARRY SULLIVAN

IT RIDES WITH THE GREAT WESTERNS!

THE WEST HAS NEVER SEEN A TEAM LIKE THIS
OR THE HUNT THAT AIMS TO DESTROY THEM!

Co-starring HARRY CAREY, JR   ROBERT DONNER   CHARLES McGREGOR   Guest Appearance by DANA ANDREWS
...duced by HARRY BERNSEN   Directed by ANTHONY M. DAWSON   Written by ERIC BERCOVICI and JERRY LUDWIG   Music by JERRY GOLDSMITH

PG PARENTAL GUIDANCE SUGGESTED
SOME MATERIAL MAY NOT BE
SUITABLE FOR PRE-TEENAGERS   COLOR BY DE LUXE ·

1031. Title?

1032. In what film did Jim Brown co-star with Raquel Welch and Burt Reynolds?

1033. In what film did Lee Van Cleef co-star with Clint Eastwood and Eli Wallach?

1034. In what film did Barry Sullivan play Ginger Rogers' psychiatrist?

1035. In what film did Dana Andrews fight a giant medieval devil?

The supreme suspense of a woman wronged beyond words, almost beyond revenge...

PARAMOUNT PICTURES AND KURT UNGER PRESENT

SOPHIA LOREN

IN

TECHNICOLOR®
PANAVISION®

CO STARRING
PETER FINCH · JACK HAWKINS

PRODUCED BY · DIRECTED BY · SCREENPLAY BY · FROM A STORY BY · MUSIC SCORED BY
KURT UNGER · DANIEL MANN · JOHN MICHAEL HAYES · LAWRENCE DURRELL · SOL KAPLAN

1036. Title?

1037. For what film did Sophia Loren receive an Academy Award?

1038. In which film did Peter Finch play a rich thief who was converted by Alec Guinness?

1039. In which film did Jack Hawkins play the editor of a Fleet Street newspaper?

1040. What was Daniel Mann's first film, based on a William Inge play and co-starring Burt Lancaster?

(70 points: answers on pages 166–8.)

Split Personalities

In each group, all the players have had a go at the same much-filmed character. Which one? In the starred cases, you get an extra point for naming the film.

1041–2. Bela Lugosi, Christopher Lee, Peter Sellers*.

1043. Ramon Novarro, Stewart Granger, Peter Sellers.

1044. John Barrymore, Melvyn Douglas, Charles Korvin.

1045–8. Charles Laughton*, Peter Ustinov*, Peter Lorre*.

1049–50. Roland Winters, Ross Martin, Peter Ustinov*.

1051. Ronald Colman, Ray Milland, John Howard.

1052. Cesar Romero, Gilbert Roland, Duncan Renaldo.

1053. Donald Cook, Eddie Quillan, Ralph Bellamy.

1054–6. Vincent Price*, Jon Hall, Arthur Franz*.

1057–60. Biff Elliott*, Ralph Meeker*, Armand Assante*.

(20 points: answers on pages 168–9.)

Who Wrote The Book?

Some of our best-remembered movies were adapted from best-selling books. Can you remember what famous (or once-famous) authors wrote the originals of the following?

1061. *The Maltese Falcon.*

1062. *Rebecca.*

1063. *Magnificent Obsession.*

1064. *Stella Dallas.*

1065. *Airport.*

1066. *The Robe.*

1067. *Dracula.*

1068. *The Prisoner of Zenda.*

1069. *The Old Dark House.*

1070. *Quo Vadis?*

1071. *Duel in the Sun.*

1072. *Ben Hur.*

1073. *The Virginian.*

1074. *Beau Geste.*

1075. *The Razor's Edge.*

1076. *Random Harvest.*

1077. *The Thirty-Nine Steps.*

1078. *The Woman in White.*

1079. *Captain Blood.*

1080. *Mr Blandings Builds His Dream House.*

(20 points: answers on page 169.)

The following novels and plays have been filmed at least twice.
Can you name their authors?

1081. *The Philadelphia Story* (play).

1082. *The Lost World* (novel).

1083. *The Bat* (play and novel).

1084. *Goodbye Mr Chips* (novel).

1085. *Mrs Wiggs of the Cabbage Patch* (novel).

1086. *The Cat and the Canary* (play).

1087. *The Four Feathers* (novel).

1088. *The Lady Vanishes* (novel).

1089. *The Phantom of the Opera* (novel).

1090. *Anna Karenina* (novel).

1091. *Lost Horizon* (novel).

1092. *The Wizard of Oz* (novel).

1093. *Back Street* (novel).

1094. *The Spiral Staircase* (novel).

1095. *The Glass Menagerie* (play).

1096. *Gaslight* (play).

1097. *The Front Page* (play).

1098. *Crime and Punishment* (novel).

1099. *The Blue Bird* (play).

1100. *Night Must Fall* (play).

(20 points: answers on pages 169–70.)

Include Me Out

There are all kinds of reasons why actors abandon a role after being cast and sometimes starting shooting. Name the films on which the following replacements occurred:

1101. Dudley Moore replaced George Segal.

1102. W. C. Fields replaced Charles Laughton.

1103. Betty Hutton replaced Judy Garland.

1104. Ray Walston replaced Peter Sellers.

1105. Fred Astaire replaced Gene Kelly.

1106. Errol Flynn replaced Robert Donat.

1107. John Gilbert replaced Laurence Olivier.

1108. Olivia de Havilland replaced Joan Crawford.

1109. Humphrey Bogart replaced Ronald Reagan.

1110. Rex Harrison replaced Christopher Plummer.

(10 points: answers on pages 170–1.)

A few questions for late at night:

1111. Who played *The Werewolf of London* in 1934?

1112. Why was Rondo Hatton, who died in 1946, thought by Universal during the last three years of his life to be so useful an ingredient of their horror films?

1113. In what film did Martita Hunt play the mother of a vampire?

1114. Who played her son?

1115. Who played the mummy in *The Mummy's Hand* (1940)?

1116. Who played Frankenstein in *Frankenstein Meets the Wolf Man*?

1117. In *Dark Eyes of London*, who dubbed Bela Lugosi's voice when he was supposed to be a gentle Englishman?

1118. On what famous play was *The House of Long Shadows* (1983) based.

1119. Richard Wordsworth in *The Quatermass Experiment* turned into a walking cactus. Where was he finally cornered?

1120. What Universal monster was played by Ricou Browning?

(10 points: answers on page 171.)

The Common Touch

Given below are lists of films in threes. The films in each trio have something in common: a theme, perhaps, or a circumstance of production, or a principal location. Can you name it in each case?

1121. *The Conqueror*: *Kotch*: *Rachel, Rachel*.

1122. *Madame Satan*: *Hell's Angels*: *The Assassination Bureau*.

1123. *Random Harvest*: *Spellbound*: *Mister Buddwing*.

1124. *Nine Hours to Rama*: *Sarajevo*: *Julius Caesar*.

1125. *La Belle Americaine*: *The Love Bug*: *Genevieve*.

1126. *Professor Mamlock*: *Crossfire*: *Gentleman's Agreement*.

1127. *The Bishop's Wife*: *The Horn Blows at Midnight*: *Forever Darling*.

1128. *The Man Between*: *The Quiller Memorandum*: *I Am a Camera*.

1129. *The Voice of Bugle Ann*: *Owd Bob*: *You Never Can Tell*.

1130. *Suddenly*: *The Man Who Knew Too Much*: *The Day of the Jackal*.

1131. *White Nights*: *La Mort du Cygne*: *The Spectre of the Rose*.

1132. *Angels in the Outfield*: *Fear Strikes Out*: *Damn Yankees*.

1133. *Detective Story*: *Saturday Night and Sunday Morning*: *Love With the Proper Stranger*.

1134. *Charlie Bubbles*: *The Lady in the Lake*: *On Approval*.

1135. *Madison Avenue*: *Good Neighbour Sam*: *The Hucksters*.

1136. *The Wizard of Oz*: *Charlie Bubbles*: *Mysterious Island*.

1137. *Man of Conquest*: *San Antonio*: *The Last Command*.

1138. *The Small Back Room*: *The Country Girl*: *Under Capricorn*.

1139. *Whisky Galore* (the captain): *David Copperfield* (the vicar): *The Scoundrel* (the literary friend).

1140. *Round the Rugged Rocks*: *Snakes and Ladders*: *Homeward Borne*.

(20 points: answers on pages 171–2.)

A few elementary questions:

1141. Who played Von Bork in *Sherlock Holmes and the Voice of Terror*?

1142. On what story was the above film based?

1143. In *Sherlock Holmes in Washington*, in what was the 'McGuffin' concealed?

1144. Who played Moriarty in *The Woman in Green*?

1145. Who played Watson in the Hammer version of *The Hound of the Baskervilles*?

1146. In what film did Basil Rathbone tell Nigel Bruce 'Olsen and Johnson are coming'?

1147. Arthur Wontner played Holmes in a version of *The Valley of Fear*. What was the film's title?

1148. Who played Holmes in *Sherlock Holmes in New York*?

1149. What did *The Scarlet Claw* turn out to be?

1150. Who played Watson in *Murder By Decree*?

(10 points: answers on page 172.)

In what film about Hollywood did:

1151. Gregory Ratoff play studio boss Herman Glogauer?

1152. Adolphe Menjou play studio boss Oliver Niles?

1153. Adolphe Menjou play studio boss Oliver Merlin?

1154. Alan Mowbray play a director called Koslofski?

1155. John Barrymore play a producer called Duncan DeGrasse?

1156. Ralph Bellamy play a producer (or studio supervisor) called C. Elliott Friday?

1157. Clifton Webb play a matinée idol called Bruce Blair?

1158. Walter Abel play studio boss G. B. DeSoto?

1159. Humphrey Bogart play a screenwriter called Dixon Steele?

1160. Peter Finch play a director called Lewis Zarkan?

(10 points: answers on page 173.)

Which 'best actors' (according to the Academy of Motion Picture Arts and Sciences) won Oscars in the years given, and for what films?

1161–2. In 1942, he impersonated a famous hero of World War I.

1163–4. In 1935, he played a traitorous member of the IRA, who died after a night of anguish.

1165–6. In 1940, he got drunk with a bride-to-be, not his own.

1167–8. In 1947, he took his thespian duties too seriously and strangled a waitress.

1169–70. In 1976, he announced to the world that he was mad as hell.

1171–2. In 1955, he played a butcher whose life was changed on a Saturday night.

1173–4. In 1968, he played a mental incompetent who was briefly cured.

1175–6. In 1930, he played a British prime minister who also played Cupid on the side.

1177–8. In 1946, he came home from the war to a good job in the bank.

1179–80. In 1942, he sang 'Little Johnny Jones' and met the president.

1181–2. In 1948, he killed his uncle and told the girl who loved him to go to a nunnery.

1183–4. In 1932, he was a boozy boxer who adopted an orphan.

1185–6. In 1929, he was the Cisco Kid in a primitive talkie of which one critic said that the sound of eggs and bacon frying was clearer than the dialogue.

1187–8. In 1933, he tossed chicken bones over his shoulder and spent his honeymoon night playing cards.

1189–90. In 1974 he shared the honours – and the title – with a cat.

1191–2. In 1954, he played Terry Malloy and was beaten up by Johnny Friendly's mob.

1193–4. In 1971, he was known as Popeye Doyle and got involved in a frantic chase around New York.

1195–6. In 1964, he made a wager with Colonel Pickering and set himself up as a rival to Freddy Eynsford-Hill.

1197–8. In 1952, he watched the seconds tick away as danger neared, and was finally saved by his bride-to-be.

1199–1200. In 1952, he called the woman he came to love a skinny old maid, and had trouble with leeches.

1201–2. In 1937, he won his second Oscar for playing his second bewhiskered European.

1203–4. In 1934, he caused a fashion sensation when he took off his shirt and revealed that he wore no undervest.

1205–6. In 1939, he aged from his twenties to his eighties and excelled in Latin.

1207–8. In 1938, he played a real-life priest with an Irish name.

1209–10. In 1931, he was an alcoholic lawyer who allowed his daughter to consort with a gangster.

(50 points: answers on pages 173–4.)

These Oscar-winning ladies, and their films, are what you have to name.

1211–12. In 1938, she scandalized society by wearing a red dress (in a black and white film).

1213–14. In 1942, she had a husband named Clem and coolly handled a Nazi parachutist.

1215–16. In 1944, she discovered that like King Lear you can do too much for ungrateful children.

1217–18. In 1932, she was told of her incurable illness by Robert Young, playing her doctor son.

1219–20. In 1935, she played a drunken actress in a film later remade as *Singapore Woman*.

1221–2. In 1948, as a deaf mute, she was helped by a country doctor.

1223–4. In 1974, she went wandering with her son and became a waitress.

1225–6. In 1966, she called her home a dump and stayed up all night to fight with her husband.

1227–8. In 1953, instead of becoming queen for a day, she gave up being a princess.

1229–30. In 1965, she was the darling of the media, but her private life suffered.

1231–2. In 1952, she bemoaned a lost dog and supported an ex-alcoholic husband.

1233–4. In 1951, she depended heavily on the kindness of strangers.

1235–6. In 1956, she made a Hollywood comeback as a woman who might or might not have descended from a famous royal line.

1237–8. In 1943, she thought she was going mad, as had Diana Wynyard before her.

1239–40. In 1937 she won her second consecutive award, this time as an oriental peasant.

1241–2. In 1933, she was a stage-struck young actress called Eva Lovelace, making her debut in New York.

1243–4. In 1949, she finally declared her independence of men.

1245–6. In 1939, she refused to think today about what she might think about tomorrow.

1247–8. In 1940, she played a white-collar girl and never danced a step.

1249–50. In 1941, she refused the bedtime drink prepared by her husband.

1251–2. In 1936, she won the award for her first Hollywood film, on the basis of a 'telephone scene'.

1253–4. In 1934, she was separated by the walls of Jericho from an actor playing a character called Peter Warne.

1255–6. In 1950, she thought she was only good at playing cards, but discovered she was more intelligent than her friends told her.

1257–8. In 1957, she played one person with several personalities.

1259–60. In 1960, she was a call girl with a well-known telephone number.

1261–2. In 1930, she played the harassed wife of a boozy old waterfront character, and was concerned for her daughter.

1263–4. In 1972, she found Berlin a little more than she bargained for.

1265–6. In 1973 she helped – or perhaps hindered – George Segal with his back trouble.

1267–8. In 1968, she presided at Christmas festivities in 1186.

1269–70. In 1969, she felt capable of directing the lives of others despite being a little past her prime.

(60 points: answers on pages 174–5.)

Colourful Titles

Explain how the following titles related to the plots or themes of the films concerned:

1271. *The Pink Panther.*

1272. *The Blue Angel.*

1273. *Green Ice.*

1274. *The Blue Lamp.*

1275. *The Red Badge of Courage.*

1276. *The Blue Gardenia.*

1277. *The Red Danube.*

1278. *The Green Man.*

1279. *The Black Bird.*

1280. *The Blue Dahlia.*

(10 points: answers on page 175.)

Strength
Of Character

Some movie characters stay in the mind more vividly than the actors who played them. Can you name the players behind the following recurrent screen personalities?

1281. Old Mother Riley.

1282. The Lone Wolf (*after* the first two talkies in 1935 and 1938, which starred Melvyn Douglas and Francis Lederer).

1283. Dagwood Bumstead (in the *Blondie* series).

1284. Inspector Lestrade (in the updated Sherlock Holmes series).

1285. Alf Garnett (in *Till Death Do Us Part* and *The Alf Garnett Saga*).

1286. Pa Kettle (in *The Egg and I* and eight following films).

1287. Maisie.

1288. Boston Blackie.

1289. The Crime Doctor.

1290. The Whistler.

(10 points: answers on pages 175–6.)

Crystal Balls _easy_

Identify these instances of cinematic crystal-gazing:

1291. In 1965, Eddie Constantine starred in a Jean-Luc Godard fantasy about a city in which computers rule.

1292. In 1969, the creator of the later *Star Wars* pictured Robert Duvall as the one sane man in a sterile future world.

1293. In 1960, Rod Taylor clashed with the Morlocks and got little help from the Eloi.

1294. In 1926, Brigitte Helm played a robot in Fritz Lang's vision of a machine-dominated city of the future.

1295. In 1930, El Brendel played a man who, after fifty years in deep freeze, woke up in 1980.

1296. In 1936, Raymond Massey and Edward Chapman played 21st-century descendants of their original characters, and watched their children leave for the moon in a rocket.

1297. In 1966, Oskar Werner played a fireman of the future, whose job is to start fires rather than extinguish them.

1298. In 1973, Charlton Heston played a 21st-century detective who discovers that the government is recycling human bodies as food.

1299. In 1979, Paul Newman took part in a game in which the winner was the one who managed to kill all the other players.

1300. In 1975, James Caan played a skilful participant in a violent game devised by government as a means of diverting the masses from political activity.

(10 points: answers on page 176.)

New adaptations from the works of Charles Dickens are ever on the way. See what you remember of the old ones.

1301. Tony Newley plays the dwarfish Quilp in the latest version of *The Old Curiosity Shop*. Who had the role in the 1935 British version directed by Thomas Bentley?

1302. What Dickens role have Finlay Currie and James Mason in common?

1303. And which has been played by both Lionel Barrymore and Michael Redgrave?

1304. And by Alastair Sim and Albert Finney?

1305. In 1930 a Paramount modern drama starring George Bancroft, called *Rich Man's Folly*, turned out to have borrowed its plot from a Dickens novel. Which?

1306. Claude Rains played in only one Dickens film, and he was the villain. What was it called?

1307. In the forties Cedric Hardwicke came back from Hollywood to Ealing to play another Dickens villain. Name the novel.

1308. Which Dickens hero was played as a boy by Anthony Wager?

1309. And which by Freddie Bartholemew?

1310. Which Dickens novel was filmed in 1934 by Universal in Hollywood, with a cast headed by Phillips Holmes, Henry Hull, Jane Wyatt and Alan Hale?

1311. And which by MGM in 1938, starring Reginald Owen?

1312. It's well known that W. C. Fields played Mr Micawber in the 1934 version of *David Copperfield*; but who played Mrs Micawber?

1313. In the same film, who played David as a man?

1314. And who appeared as Aunt Betsy Trotwood?

1315. A British actor played twins in a Dickens film of the forties, and in the early fifties took the leading role in another. Name him.

1316. What much-filmed novel (sound versions in 1936 and 1958) was also very successful as a 1917 silent starring William Farnum?

1317. In what Dickens novel, filmed twice since World War II, do the following characters appear: Mr Brownlow, Mr Bumble, Mr Grimwig, Mr Sowerberry?

1318. Which of these actors has *not* played a Dickens hero? Derek Bond, Dirk Bogarde, Richard Attenborough or John Mills?

1319. Alec Guinness is well remembered as Fagin in *Oliver Twist*, and more recently played Marley's Ghost in *Scrooge*. His first notable screen appearance was also in a Dickens role. Name it.

1320. Emlyn Williams was well known as Dickens on the stage, but only once played a Dickens role in a film, and then it was originally intended for TV. Name it.

(20 points: answers on pages 176–7.)

My Life In Print

Which actors wrote autobiographies under the following titles?

1321. *Bulls, Balls, Bicycles and Actors.*

1322. *I.D.*

1323. *All My Yesterdays.*

1324. *Dead End Yells, Wedding Bells, Cockle Shells and Dizzy Spells.*

1325. *My Wicked, Wicked Ways.*

1326. *Past Imperfect.*

1327. *An Actor and His Time.*

1328. *Wide-Eyed in Babylon.*

1329. *A Proper Job.*

1330. *Anything for a Quiet Life.*

1331. *Memoirs of a Professional Cad.*

1332. *Let the Chips Fall.*

1333. *Sparks Fly Upward.*

1334. *Out on a Limb.*

1335. *The Eternal Male.*

1336. *I Like What I Know.*

1337. *Life is a Banquet.*

1338. *Intermission.*

1339. *The Movies, Mr Griffith, and Me.*

1340. *Where's the Rest of Me?*

(20 points: answers on pages 177–8.)

Name the film in which the listed star played the listed performer:

1341. Susan Hayward played Jane Froman.

1342. Susan Hayward played Lilian Roth.

1343. Danny Kaye played Red Nichols.

1344. Frank Sinatra played Joe E. Lewis.

1345. James Cagney made a guest appearance (only) as George M. Cohan.

1346. Kathryn Grayson played Grace Moore.

1347. Mitzi Gaynor played Eva Tanguay.

1348. Mitzi Gaynor played Lotta Crabtree.

1349. Nat King Cole played W. C. Handy.

1350. Monty Woolley played Monty Woolley.

(10 points: answers on page 178.)

States Of The Union

One can scarcely imagine British films calling themselves
Lancashire! or *Suffolk!* But here are ten American movies which
used the names of states in their titles. Given three principal
members of the cast, and the date, can you name them?

1351. 1946: Ray Milland, Barbara Stanwyck, Barry Fitzgerald.

1352. 1952: Lew Ayres, Marilyn Maxwell, Robert Hutton.

1353. 1941: Jean Arthur, William Holden, Warren William.

1354. 1929: Warren Baxter, Edmund Lowe, Dorothy Burgess.

1355. 1956: Gordon MacRae, Shirley Jones, Rod Steiger.

1356. 1945: Barbara Stanwyck, Dennis Morgan, Sydney
Greenstreet.

1357. 1966: Max Von Sydow, Julie Andrews, Richard Harris.

1358. 1977: Liza Minnelli, Robert de Niro, Lionel Stander.

1359. 1941: William Holden, Claire Trevor, Edgar Buchanan.

1360. 1941: Bob Hope, Vera Zorina, Victor Moore.

(10 points: answers on page 178.)

It Takes Two To Tango

Various pairs of actors – and I'm thinking of one male, one female – have been found to play so well together that they are cast as a team in several films. Can you name both players in each of the following groups?

1361–2. *Practically Yours, Family Honeymoon, No Time For Love, Maid of Salem.*

1363–4. *Rationing, Bad Bascomb, Jackass Mail, Barnacle Bill.*

1365–6. *Colleen, Dames, Flirtation Walk, Shipmates Forever.*

1367–8. *Too Young To Kiss, The Bride Goes Wild, Remains to be Seen, Two Girls and a Sailor.*

1369–70. *Parnell, Test Pilot, Manhattan Melodrama, Men in White.*

1371–2. *Possessed, Chained, Strange Cargo, Dancing Lady.*

1373–4. *Model Wife, I Want a Divorce, Broadway Gondolier, Gold Diggers of 1937.*

1375–6. *Trooper Hook, The Great Man's Lady, Gambling Lady, Banjo on my Knee.*

1377–8. *Don't Trust Your Husband, Honeymoon in Bali, Café Society, Virginia.*

1379–80. *The Man Who Came Back, Sunny Side Up, Delicious, Street Angel.*

The titles are not necessarily in chronological order.

(20 points: answers on page 179.)

Hollywood once had a vast repertory of character actors who played in support of the stars. Just now and again one of them would fall gratefully upon a role which enabled him or her to upstage the stars and get all the notices. Can you name the actors who were so good as . . .

1381. Professor Moriarty in *The Adventures of Sherlock Holmes* (1939)?

1382. Ma Joad in *The Grapes of Wrath* (1940)?

1383. Clarence, the angel, in *It's a Wonderful Life* (1946)?

1384. Veronica Lake's sorcerer father in *I Married a Witch* (1942)?

1385. Mr Collins, the pompous clergyman, in *Pride and Prejudice* (1940)?

1386. 'Concentration Camp' Erhardt in *To Be or Not To Be* (1942)?

1387. Seth Lord, Katharine Hepburn's father, in *The Philadelphia Story* (1940)?

1388. Uncle Pio, the philosophical lavatory attendant, in *Gilda* (1946)?

1389. Madame Von Eln, Robert Cummings' grandmother, in *King's Row* (1941)?

1390. Griselda the witch in *The Court Jester* (1955)?

1391. His Excellency, lord of Hades, in *Heaven Can Wait* (1943)?

1392. Inspector Hubbard, the man with the nail scissors, in *Dial M For Murder* (1954)?

1393. Pirovitch, the nervous shop assistant, in *The Shop Around the Corner* (1940)?

1394. Miss Habersham, the dogged old lady who helps solve the murder in *Intruder in the Dust* (1949)?

1395. Edythe Van Hopper, the gorgon to whom Joan Fontaine is companion at the beginning of *Rebecca* (1940)?

1396. Ma Jarrett, the fearsome parent whose death sends Cagney to pieces in *White Heat* (1948)?

1397. Wilmer, the nervous 'gunsel' chaffed by Humphrey Bogart in *The Maltese Falcon* (1941)?

1398. Professor Van Helsing, the vampire hunter, in *Dracula* (1930)?

1399. Judy Garland's grandfather in *Meet Me in St Louis* (1944)?

1400. Bernstein, the accident-prone business manager, in *Citizen Kane* (1941)?

(20 points: answers on pages 179–80.)

Keep It In The Family

Each pair of films represents a father – child relationship: the father was in the first, the child in the second. No dates are given – that would make it too easy. One mark per surname.

1401. *Sunnyside; Dr Zhivago.*

1402. *Letter of Introduction; The Group.*

1403. *Tell It to the Marines; Weird Woman.*

1404. *The Green Light; Son of Captain Blood.*

1405. *The Quiet American; Isadora.*

1406. *It's Great to be Young; Sky West and Crooked.*

1407. *Rhapsody in Blue; Sweet Liberty.*

1408. *A Letter to Three Wives; Running.*

1409. *Mary Poppins; Kiss Me Kate.*

1410. *Playmates; The Big Night.*

(10 points: answers on page 180.)

Step Into My Shoes

We are dealing here with films which have suffered at least two remakes. One point in each case for naming the original property from the clues we give you, which in each case are the names of three players who acted the same role in different versions. An extra point for naming any changed titles, which are indicated by extra squares.

1411–13. Edward G. Robinson, Raymond Massey, Barry Sullivan.

1414–15. Douglass Montgomery, Robert Taylor, John Kerr.

1416. Joseph Schildkraut, Allan Jones, Howard Keel.

1417. Fredric March, James Mason, Kris Kristofferson.

1418–19. Fredric March, Spencer Tracy, Paul Massie.

1420–1. Bebe Daniels, Bette Davis, Mary Astor.

1422–4. Jean Harlow, Ann Sothern, Ava Gardner.

1425–7. Joel McCrea, John Loder, Richard Widmark.

1428–9. Norma Shearer, Joan Crawford, Greer Garson.

1430. Walter Abel, Don Ameche, Michael York.

(20 points: answers on pages 180–1.)

Forever Ealing

Ealing is still a magic word among those who care for the best in British films. Can you recognize these Ealing films from the descriptions given?

1431. Released in 1946, it told of men existing in a 'little wire-enclosed cinder patch'. The women who waited for them included Rachel Kempson and Jane Barrett.

1432. Advertised in 1951 as 'a drama of the river underworld', it took itself seriously but had part of its original script diverted to form the basis of one of the studio's most scintillating comedies. Bonar Colleano and Susan Shaw headed the cast.

1433. 'The secrets of a street you know', boasted the advertising for this 1947 melodrama. Often claimed as the first piece of British neo-realism, its suspenseful picture of East End low life is as thrilling today as it was then.

1434. Advertised in 1950 as concerning 'the unending battle of the city streets', this police thriller set in the Paddington area of London was not only an immense popular success but spawned a long-running television series.

1435. 'It pokes fun at the Hun!' was the inducement to see this 1942 farce with Will Hay in a dual role. Peter Ustinov could be observed among his Nazi pupils.

1436. Promoted as 'the story of a ghostly inn', this thoughtful drama had clear affinities with the later *Brigadoon*. Tom Walls and Glynis Johns were prominent among the cast, in 1943.

1437. 'Laughter, love, suspense and thrills in a film of a fateful journey' were offered in this rather mild brew which offered little of anything in its three interwoven stories. Peter Finch and Jack Warner were among those involved, in 1949.

1438. This 'romance that rocked the throne of kings' was the oft-told story of Konigsmark, but the film's title cancelled out the attraction of period trappings and Technicolor. Joan Greenwood and Stewart Granger starred, in 1948.

119

1439. 'The men who broke the bank – and lost the cargo' got caught in the end, for the censor insisted in 1951; but the end barely spoiled the audience's enjoyment. Can you guess the title without being given the stars?

1440. This 'spectacular drama of Australia's gold rush' made little impact in 1948, coming towards the end of Ealing's antipodean period. Chips Rafferty and Gordon Jackson were featured.

(10 points: answers on pages 181–2.)

Titled Ladies

A star is sometimes thought to have 'arrived' when a film is named after his or her character. Who, then, played the following title roles?

1441. *Janie* in 1944?

1442. *Jessica* in 1962?

1443. *Diane* in 1956?

1444. *Nana* in 1934?

1445. *Louisa* in 1950?

1446. *Teresa* in 1951?

1447. *Cynthia* in 1947?

1448. *Ramona* in 1936?

1449. *Ivy* in 1947?

1450. *Frenchie* in 1950?

(10 points: answers on pages 182–3.)

Titled Gents

Movies are also named after male characters, but for them a first name is seldom thought sufficient. What stars played the following title roles?

1451. *Billy the Kid* in 1930?

1452. *Mister Cory* in 1957?

1453. *Kid Galahad* in 1937?

1454. *Old Hutch* in 1936?

1455. *Dr Broadway* in 1942?

1456. *Lucky Jordan* in 1942?

1457. *Jack Slade* in 1953?

1458. *Frankenstein* in 1931?

1459. *Elmer the Great* in 1933?

1460. *Alexander Hamilton* in 1931?

(10 points: answers on page 183.)

The British
Are Coming!

Until the seventies it was rare for British films to win major Academy Awards – but these movies did. Can you say in which category, and (for an additional point) who made each film?

1461–2. *The Seventh Veil* (1945).

1463–4. *Goodbye Mr Chips* (1939).

1465–6. *The Third Man* (1949).

1467–8. *49th Parallel* (1941).

1469–70. *Sons and Lovers* (1960).

1471–2. *The Lavender Hill Mob* (1951).

1473–4. *Seven Days to Noon* (1950).

1475–6. *Pygmalion* (1938).

1477–8. *Room at the Top* (1959).

1479–80. *The V.I.P.s* (1963).

(20 points: answers on pages 183–4.)

1481–4. What girls played boys more or less throughout the following films? *As You Like It*: *Sylvia Scarlett*: *Sullivan's Travels*: *Wings of the Morning*.

1485–6. Name the 1962 film, and its producer/director, in which the lead was taken by a person of indeterminate sex named Jean Arless, heard of neither before nor since.

1487. What famous drag role was played on film in 1930 by Charles Ruggles, in 1940 by Arthur Askey and in 1942 by Jack Benny?

1488–9. Name the title, and the star, of the musical version which emerged in 1952.

1490. What famous comedian was impersonated by Gloria Swanson in *Sunset Boulevard*?

1491. What famous comedy team was impersonated in *The Killing of Sister George* by Susannah York and Beryl Reid?

1492. What comedian impersonated Alice Faye in the 'Slumming on Park Avenue' number in *On the Avenue*?

1493–4. What comedian posing as a not-so-gorgeous blonde was tossed around by apache dancer Anthony Caruso in what 1941 service comedy?

1495–6. What brothers played gypsy chorus girls – unconvincingly – in what 1935 extravaganza?

1497–8. Who and in what film had to wear Katharine Hepburn's negligée when his own clothes had been sent to the cleaners? And what excuse did he give to May Robson?

1500. In what fantasy melodrama of 1936 did Lionel Barrymore spend much of his time disguised as an old woman?

1501. Name Lon Chaney's last film, in which he was a criminal in female disguise?

1502. Who played the headmistress, Miss Millicent Fritton, in *The Belles of St Trinians*?

1503–5. In *Star Spangled Rhythm* Paulette Goddard, Dorothy Lamour and Veronica Lake satirized their own trade-marks in a number called 'A Sweater, a Sarong and a Peek-a-boo Bang'. It was then reprised by three character comedians in drag. Who were they?

1506. Elspeth Dudgeon is not in the cast list of James Whale's 1932 film *The Old Dark House*, but plays a vital role. Explain.

1507–10. Julie Andrews in the 1982 film *Victor/Victoria* played a woman playing a man whom everybody thought was a woman . . . or something like that. Name the two previous versions of this story, and the stars who took the lead.

1511. In what film did Elizabeth Taylor pretend to be of the opposite sex?

1512. In which of his films did Will Hay don the costume of a female nurse?

1513. In the episode of *The Man From Uncle* called *The Mother Muffin Affair*, who played the title role?

1514. Who in *Babes on Broadway* impersonated Carmen Miranda?

1515. In what film did Marlene Dietrich, as a White Russian countess, cross the border disguised as a Cossack officer?

1516. Who played the transvestite Frank N. Furter in *The Rocky Horror Picture Show*?

1517. Name the 1968 remake of *The Paleface* in which Don Knotts disguised himself as an Indian squaw.

1518. The outlaw Belle Starr, who wore men's clothes, was played with glamour in 1940 by Gene Tierney. Who, as *Montana Belle* in 1952, played her with more realism?

1519. What mannish western character was played realistically in 1931 by Louise Dresser in *Caught*, and romantically in 1953 by Doris Day in a film titled after the character?

1520. In the 1936 version of *As You Like It*, in which Laurence Olivier played Orlando, who was Rosalind, the banished duke's daughter who poses as a shepherd's boy?

(40 points: answers on pages 184–5.)

Spectacular dramas are always popular, with subjects ranging from fires to earthquakes. The following questions check your rating on past films of this kind. Fifteen correct answers and you're a film buff. Ten – and you're doing pretty well. Five? Well, you're obviously too young to remember.

1521. In what film was Bette Davis caught up in the San Francisco earthquake of 1906?

1522. In what film did Rod Taylor play a pilot whose apparent error caused a passenger plane to crash on take-off, starting an enquiry which – with flashbacks – occupied the entire film?

1523. Name the film in which Linda Darnell fled from the great London fire of 1666.

1524. In *The Good Earth*, life and livelihood were threatened by a plague of . . . what?

1525. What kind of disaster was featured in *The Brave Don't Cry*, *The Proud Valley* and *Black Fury*?

1526. In *The Day the Earth Caught Fire*, why did it?

1527. In what film did John Mills and Richard Attenborough figure among the party trapped in a submarine at the bottom of the sea?

1528. What natural phenomenon threatened the cast of *The Devil at Four o'clock*?

1529. Name the science-fiction producer responsible for, among others, *When Worlds Collide*, *The War of the Worlds* and *Conquest of Space*.

1530. A recent catastrophe film was taken from a novel by Paul Gallico, directed by Robert Neame, and starred (among others) Carol Lynley, Red Buttons and Roddy McDowall. Name it.

1531. Which of Cecil B. De Mille's epics climaxed in a train wreck?

1532. Name the actor playing the villain, who had fought Clark Gable for Jeanette Macdonald's hand and died in the earthquake in *San Francisco* (1936)?

1533. Name the fifties remake of *The Rains Came*, starring Lana Turner and Richard Burton.

1534. What athletic hero began his star career in *The Hurricane* (1938)?

1535. In which silent film by D. W. Griffith was the fall of Babylon depicted?

1536. A disaster was narrowly averted in what film starring (among others) Helen Hayes as a stowaway and Van Heflin as a mad bomber?

1537. A British film about a sea disaster featured many well-known actors and actresses including Michael Goodliffe, David McCallum, Honor Blackman and Alec McCowen. The star's name is withheld: name the film.

1538. What kind of disaster is common to *The Bluebird* and *Bambi*?

1539. In what film did Roland Young stop the world from moving?

1540. Which historical character – allegedly responsible for starting a celebrated disaster – has been played by Peter Lorre, Peter Ustinov and Charles Laughton?

(20 points: answers on page 185.)

One hundred answers are required to the miscellaneous questions below. It's a last chance to add some quick points: see how you get on.

1541. Billy Wilder originally wanted Charles Laughton to play the café proprietor in *Irma La Douce*: who got the part?

1542. Who played the disillusioned Russian official Igor Gouzenko in the 1948 film *The Iron Curtain*?

1543–6. Jack Le Vien, an American producer in London, became friendly with Winston Churchill and the Duke of Windsor. Can you name the documentary features which resulted? (Two for Churchill, plus one television series; one for the Duke.)

1547. Name the Laurel and Hardy short, made in 1930, in which the comedians play their own children.

1548–50. Warners in 1950 released a film called *The Breaking Point*. Of what 1945 Warner film was it a remake? Who wrote the original novel? Who starred in the next remake, *The Gun Runners*, made in 1958?

1551. Who was the wife in *Guest Wife* (1945)?

1552. Name the American adventurer who in the thirties appeared in such travel adventures as *Bring 'Em Back Alive* and *Jungle Menace*.

1553. Who played Lawyer Crosby, first to die in the 1939 version of *The Cat and the Canary*?

1554. In 1955, Stewart Granger and Jean Simmons tried to murder each other in an adaptation of a W. W. Jacobs story called *The Interruption*. Name it.

1555–6. Who played Jane Eyre in the 1934 version of the story? And who Rochester?

1557. In 1973 Stephen Sondheim and Anthony Perkins co-authored a murder mystery set on a millionaire's yacht. Name it.

1558. Name the 1943 film (not released until 1946) in which Sydney Greenstreet played William Makepeace Thackeray.

1559–62. A 1976 TV movie, *Reflections of Murder*, starred Tuesday Weld, Joan Hackett and Sam Waterston. Who played these roles in the French film from which it was adapted? Give the film's title in English or French.

1563–5. William Holden and Trevor Howard in 1958 appeared in an eagerly awaited film called *The Key*. Who wrote it? Who directed it? Who was the third star?

1566–9. In 1945 Alexander Korda produced a film called *Perfect Strangers*, with Robert Donat and . . . who, as his wife? In America little was thought of the title and the film went out as *Vacation from Marriage*. In 1950 Hollywood made a film called *Perfect Strangers*, about jurors on a murder case. Who were the two stars? What was the British title of *that* film?

1570. Still on the theme of perfection, Laurence Olivier in 1933 played in a film opposite Gloria Swanson. What was the title?

1571–3. Who played Nurse Peggotty in the 1935 MGM version of *David Copperfield*? Who played Mr Dick? Who (briefly and rather unofficially) played the vicar of Blunderstone?

1574–5. In 1939 Ronald Colman starred in the film version of a story by Rudyard Kipling. Name the film, and the young English actress who played opposite him.

1576–8. In what 1968 film did David Niven play the ghostly Royal Navy captain of a ghostly World War II cruiser? Who directed it? Who was the leading lady?

1579–81. In her 1940 film *The Letter*, Bette Davis generously allowed much of the spotlight to fall on her co-star, an English actor who played her lawyer and who died soon after the film was released. Can you name him? And who played her husband? And what well-known character actor is listed among the cast at the beginning but barely visible in the crowd scene at the end, his role having been totally cut?

1582. Who played *The Thin Man*?

1583–4. The 1960 Disney version of *The Swiss Family Robinson* was a big box office hit, but who played Mr and Mrs Robinson in the 1940 version directed by Edward Ludwig?

1585. What is the setting common to the Hollywood monster movies *Tarantula*, *It Came From Outer Space* and *Them!*?

1586–7. In 1960 two American stars played the leads in an Italian hokum adventure called *The Tartars*. Can you name them?

1588–91. The success of *Written on the Wind* in 1956 caused Universal hastily to set up something similar (they hoped) for three of its stars. Name the three stars and the film.

1592. What long-serving Hollywood character actress played her last brief role as the bird woman in *Mary Poppins*?

1593–6. In 1933 Ronald Colman was *The Masquerader*. Who played the drug-addicted politician whose place he takes? Who was the politician's butler? Two years earlier, the actor playing the butler had come to grief at the hands of one of Hollywood's perennial monsters. Which one and in which film?

1597. *Le Dernier Milliardaire* (1934) was directed by Jean Renoir. True or false?

1598. Marlene Dietrich's last film – unless one counts the documentary in which, unseen, she spoke to Maximilian Schell about her films – was a 1978 curiosity directed by David Hemmings and starring David Bowie and Sidney Rome. Can you name it?

1599–1600. What famous literary characters were played by Peter O'Toole and Richard Roundtree in 1975?

1601. A highly acclaimed Franco-Italian film of 1960 starred Alain Delon, Renato Salvatori, Katina Paxinou and Annie Girardot; it was directed by Luchino Visconti and ran 180 minutes. Title, please.

1602–5. A 1950 Franco-Italian film provided a woeful end for the careers of two favourite Hollywood performers. Co-starring Suzy Delair, it was sometimes known as *Escapade* or *Utopia*; but can you name its two more familiar titles, and also name the two stars?

1606. Jerry Lewis's *Rock-a-bye Baby* (1958) was a variation on what Preston Sturges comedy of the previous decade?

1607–8. When the 1936 film *The Petrified Forest* was remade in 1945 with Nazis instead of gangsters, what was the new title? And who played the chief Nazi?

1609–10. A 1930 film called *A Lady to Love* was remade ten years later as *They Knew What They Wanted*, with Charles Laughton and Carole Lombard. Who played the roles in the original?

1611. There are two American films called *My Favorite Spy*. The 1941 film stars Bob Hope; who stars in the 1942 film?

1612–13. The first two episodes of the TV series, *The Untouchables*, about the Al Capone gangster era, were joined together and released in 1958 as a feature. Under what title? And with what actor as Capone?

1614. In what 1956 film did James Mason play Lucille Ball's guardian angel?

1615–16. In 1948 Abraham Polonsky directed and co-wrote a thriller about the numbers racket, which the script never quite managed to explain. Title and star, please.

1617–19. In Laurence Olivier's *Henry V*, who played Chorus? And who Ancient Pistol? Who composed the music?

1620. Lucille Ball was *Mame*, but who starred in the previous (1958) version called *Auntie Mame*?

1621–2. In Jean Cocteau's *Orpheus*, who played Death (the Princess)? And how did the characters reach the other world?

1623. In 1956 Marlene Dietrich and Vittorio de Sica starred in a rather dull romantic comedy directed by Samuel Taylor. Title, please.

1624–5. What animal was impersonated by Mischa Auer in *My Man Godfrey* (1936)? Who played Mr Bullock?

1626. Name the 1962 film by Luis Buñuel in which guests at a high society dinner find themselves mysteriously unable to leave.

1627. Can you name the sequel to the 1956 film *Rock Around the Clock*?

1628. Can you name the sequel to the 1953 film *The Robe*?

1629. In 1949 Ealing Studios filmed a Roy Horniman novel called *Noblesse Oblige*. What was the film's title?

1630–3. Danny Kaye had fun in *On the Riviera*, but can you name the actors who had previously played the dual role in 1935 and 1941? Can you also name the films?

1634–6. In 1932 Cecil B. De Mille made *The Sign of the Cross*, about unpleasant things happening to Christians in ancient Rome. Who played Nero? Who played Poppea, who took a bath in asses' milk? Who wrote the original play?

1637–8. What film followed *The Curse of Frankenstein* in the Hammer saga of the obsessed scientist? Who played the monster in it?

1639–40. In 1940 Cary Grant starred in a historical drama about a Virginian surveyor who finds himself involved in the revolutionary war. Give its American and British titles.

(100 points: answers on pages 185–7.)

Answers

Orientation Quiz

1–2. Charles Farrell and Janet Gaynor were so styled in 1932 □ □

3–4. Alexander; Larry Simms □ □

5–6. *The Devil and Daniel Webster*: All That Money Can Buy □ □

7–9. *Top Secret Affair*: Kirk Douglas and Susan Hayward □ □ □

10. The Baer brothers, both prizefighters. Max's big moment was *The Prizefighter and the Lady* in 1933 with Myrna Loy; Buddy's in *Quo Vadis?* □

11–14. P. T. Barnum: they were an aged black woman, Siamese twins and . . . well, nobody was quite sure. Wallace Berry: *A Lady's Morals* and *The Mighty Barnum* □ □ □ □

15–18. Barrymore: Ethel, Lionel and John □ □ □ □

19–22. Sam Bass. *Calamity Jane and Sam Bass*; *Badman's Territory*; *The Texas Rangers* □ □ □ □

23. Batman. (They played the Caped Crusader in the cinema serial.) □

24–8. Desi Arnaz; Cab Calloway; Kay Kyser; Glenn Miller; Paul Whiteman □ □ □ □ □

29. Betty Boop. Helen was the 'boop-boop-a-doop' girl □

30–31. Bert Kalmar and Harry Ruby; Debbie Reynolds □ □

32. 'Beautiful Dreamer' □

33–4. Blackbeard the Pirate; Robert Newton □ □

35. Peter Ustinov □

36. Toshiro Mifune, in Kurosawa's film □

37–8. John Carradine; Richard Burton □ □

39. Claudette Colbert, in 1938 □

40. Graham Chapman □

41. Blondie and Dagwood Bumstead □

42–3. Penny Singleton and Arthur Lake □ □

44. The East Side Kids (*not* the Bowery Boys) □

45–6. George Raft: *The Bowery* □ □

47. Buck Rogers □

48–9. Clark Gable in *It Happened One Night* □ □

50–1. Bulldog Drummond: Tom Conway □ □

52–4. *Car 54 Where Are You?* Joe E. Ross, Fred Gwynne □ □ □

55. He was the voice of Chan □

56. The Cisco Kid □

57. Columbo. The shabby detective was played on Broadway by Mitchell. Crosby was sought for TV, but Falk got the job □

58–9. James Dean: *Has Anybody Seen My Gal?* □ □

60–3. Field Marshal Erwin Rommel. Von Stroheim in *Five Graves to Cairo*; Mason in *The Desert Fox* (and *Desert Rats*); Plummer in *The Night of the Generals* □ □ □ □

64. Donald Duck □

65. Lon Chaney. His death opened the door for Bela Lugosi □

66. Bela Lugosi. He withdrew when he found he would have no lines □

67–8. Mrs Munster in *The Munsters*. Yvonne de Carlo □ □

69–75. Walter Huston; Randolph Scott; Henry Fonda; Joel McCrea; Burt Lancaster; James Garner; James Stewart □ □ □ □ □ □ □

76. Paramount News □

77. Max Brand □

78. George Arliss □

79. Paul Newman had had good luck with *The Hustler* and *Hud* and wanted another name beginning with H. He next made *Hombre* □

80–3. Dick Powell, Charles Boyer, Rosalind Russell, Joel McCrea. (The last two contributed little, and their places were more or less taken by David Niven and Jack Lemmon.) □ □ □ □

84. *Alfred Hitchcock Presents* □

85. Geronimo ☐

86. An in-joke; it's IBM one letter back in the alphabet ☐

87–90. Alfred Hitchcock: *Blackmail*; *Young and Innocent*; *North by Northwest* ☐ ☐ ☐ ☐

91. Milton Berle ☐

92–3. Clark Gable: *The Misfits* ☐ ☐

94–5. Messala: *Ben Hur* ☐ ☐

96. Rin Tin Tin ☐

97–100. Mata Hari. Greta Garbo, Jeanne Moreau, Sylvia Kristel ☐ ☐ ☐ ☐

Mr Laurel And Mr Hardy

101–2. James Finlayson: *From Soup to Nuts* ☐ ☐

103. He doesn't receive one. The credits used were those made for the featurette version ☐

104. *Should Married Men Go Home?* ☐

105. Ollie pretends to be ill so that the boys can play hookey from their wives ☐

106. *Two Tars* ☐

107. The preparations for leaving home were so funny that in the completed film the characters never get to the picnic ☐

108. In each case the boys are trying to hide an animal from their landlord ☐

109–10. *Big Business*: James Finlayson ☐ ☐

111. Jean Harlow ☐

112. *Twice Two* ☐

113. *The Private Life of Oliver the Eighth* ☐

114. Stan and Ollie are seen briefly as hitchhikers by the roadside ☐

115. *Them Thar Hills* ☐

116. *Fra Diavolo* ☐

117. *Our Relations* ☐

118. Harry Langdon ☐

119. *Our Relations* □
120. *Sons of the Desert* (a.k.a. *Fraternally Yours*) □

All Creatures Great And Small

121. Camel □
122. Cat □
123. Dog □
124. Squirrel □
125. Mule □
126. Elephant (British title: *Elephants Never Forget*) □
127. Bear □
128. Dolphin □
129. Kangaroo. (The producers couldn't find one which could act, so this sorry film ended up starring a man in a skin.) □
130. Dog owned by Laurel and Hardy (breed unspecified) □

Mind Your Ps, Never Mind The Qs

131. Puddleby-in-the-Marsh □
132. The Pushmi-pullyu □
133. Paladin □
134. Passepartout □
135. Pepe Le Pew □
136. Pyewacket □
137. Pussy Galore □
138. Parkyakarkus □
139. S. F. La Paloma □
140. Pooka □

Early Days

141. Ginger Rogers (1930) □
142. Ray Milland (1932–4) □

143. Tyrone Power (1936–7) □
144. Shelley Winters (1944) □
145. James Stewart (1935–6) □
146. Spencer Tracy (1930–31) □
147. Clark Gable (1931) □
148. Bette Davis (1931) □
149. Edward G. Robinson (1930) □
150. Joan Fontaine (1937–8) □

Slight Seconds

151–2. Herbert Marshall; lost a leg in the First World War □ □
153–4. Norma Shearer; a slight squint □ □
155–6. Harold Lloyd; lost the finger and thumb of one hand when a comedy bomb exploded □ □
157–8. Esmond Knight; blinded in the Second World War □ □
159–60. Lionel Barrymore; a fall complicated by arthritis kept him in a wheelchair from 1938 □ □
161–2. Peter Falk; one cast eye □ □
163–4. Donald Gray; lost an arm in the Second World War □ □
165–6. Ben Turpin; gloriously crossed eyes □ □
167–8. Susan Peters; confined to a wheelchair after hurting her back in a fall □ □
169–70. Robert Donat; chronic asthma (which eventually killed him) □ □

They're Either Too Young Or Too Old

171–2. David Bruce: Universal □ □
173–4. Robert Paige: Universal □ □
175–6. James Craig: MGM □ □
177–8. Turhan Bey: Universal □ □
179–80. Sonny Tufts: Paramount □ □
181–2. Dane Clark: Warner □ □

183–4. Lon McCallister: Fox ☐ ☐
185–6. William Eythe: Fox ☐ ☐
187–8. Paul Henreid: Warner ☐ ☐
189–90. Arturo de Cordova: Paramount ☐ ☐

Yanks At Oxford (and elsewhere)
191. Dean Jagger ☐
192. Jimmy Durante ☐
193. Robert Mitchum ☐
194. Robert Montgomery ☐
195. Edward Everett Horton ☐
196. Mickey Rooney ☐
197. Dane Clark ☐
198. Paul Douglas ☐
199. Tyrone Power ☐
200. Douglass Montgomery ☐

Were There No British Gels Available?
201. Edwige Feuillere ☐
202. Cornell Borchers ☐
203. Valentina Cortesa ☐
204. Julia Arnall ☐
205. Elisabeth Bergner ☐
206. Simone Signoret ☐
207. Mai Zetterling ☐
208. Michele Morgan ☐
209. Odile Versois ☐
210. Alida Valli (then known simply as Valli) ☐

Actors Should Be Treated Like . . . Gold Dust
211. *Mr and Mrs Smith* ☐
212. *Young and Innocent* ☐

213. *North by Northwest* ☐
214. *Rebecca* ☐
215. *Strangers on a Train* ☐
216. *Spellbound* ☐
217. *Saboteur* ☐
218. *I Confess* ☐
219. *The Man Who Knew Too Much* (1934) ☐
220. *The Lady Vanishes* ☐

People Of Character

221. Professor Harold Hill in *The Music Man* ☐
222. Femm ☐
223. Sidney Kidd ☐
224. Mac the night watchman ☐
225. Whiplash Willie ☐
226. The Miracle of Morgan's Creek ☐
227. Pinocchio ☐
228. Laura ☐
229. Mr Magoo ☐
230. Stan Laurel ☐

Actors We Like

231. *The Swan* ☐
232. *The Ghoul* (1933) ☐
233. *The Old Dark House* (1932) ☐
234. *The Wrong Man* ☐
235. *They Died With Their Boots On* ☐
236. *The Hunchback of Notre Dame* (1939) ☐
237. *Alias Nick Beal* ☐
238. *The Beast with Five Fingers* ☐
239. *Frenchman's Creek* ☐
240. *Gilda* ☐

Not So Leading Ladies

241. Joan Weldon ☐
242. Micheline Presle ☐
243. Florence Marly ☐
244. Nicole Maurey ☐
245. Una Merkel ☐
246. Lilo Pulver ☐
247. Peggy Moran ☐
248. Taina Elg ☐
249. Susan Shentall ☐
250. Ellen Drew ☐
251. Diane Baker ☐
252. Claudia Cardinale ☐
253. Inger Stevens ☐
254. Marie Windsor ☐
255. Carolyn Jones ☐
256. Josephine Hutchinson ☐
257. Jacqueline Bisset ☐
258. Nancy Olson ☐
259. Rosemary Lane ☐
260. Priscilla Lane ☐

When They Were Bad They Were Horrid

261–2 Paul Newman: *The Silver Chalice* ☐ ☐
263–4. Bette Davis: *Connecting Rooms* ☐ ☐
265–6. Charles Laughton: *Abbott and Costello Meet Captain Kidd* ☐ ☐
267–8. Peter Sellers: *Never Let Go* ☐ ☐
269–70. Gloria Swanson: *Three For Bedroom C* ☐ ☐
271–2. Katharine Hepburn: *Olly Olly Oxen Free* ☐ ☐
273–4. Mickey Spillane: *The Girl Hunters* ☐ ☐

275–6. James Cagney: *Johnny Come Lately* □ □

277–8. Lana Turner: *The Big Cube* □ □

279–80. Henry Fonda: *The Man Who Understood Women* □ □

What's In A Name?

281. Famous stunt man, former cowboy, latterly second unit director □

282. Orson Welles used this signature for his co-scripting of the 1971 version of *Treasure Island* □

283. A W. C. Fields nom-de-plume. Using it for his script of *The Bank Dick* he remarked that it derived from his having sat through so many upper crust English plays in which the hero said to his butler, 'My hat, my cane, Jeeves' □

284. A Peruvian singer with a wide octave range: she appeared in 1954 in *The Secret of the Incas* □

285. Two of the several noms-de-plume of scriptwriter Dalton Trumbo during the period when he was blacked as a Red □

286. Celebrated composer, long with Warners □

287. Also a composer, with Paramount in the thirties; provided a notably eerie score for *The Cat and the Canary* □

288. Art director, with RKO in the thirties □

289. British child star of the thirties □

290. Writer-producer-director from radio: films freakish □

291. Scriptwriter whose chief claim to fame is *Gilda* □

292. Character actor, senior scientist in *Frankenstein*, general know-all in *Dracula* and *The Mummy* □

293. Actor (*Quatermass II*, Jonathan Harker in the 1958 *Dracula*) who turned executive producer for Columbia □

294. 'One-take Woody', long a reliable director for MGM □

295. Brought from Broadway, he directed a couple of forties films for Warner; but *The Enforcer* was allegedly completed by Raoul Walsh □

296. Costume designer of the golden age □

297. Another Broadway-to-Warner director, chiefly remembered for *Between Two Worlds* (1944) □

298. Cinematographer, long with Twentieth Century Fox ☐
299. Dance director, notably for Fred Astaire ☐
300. Composer who scored a few Hollywood films, notably the 1945 version of *And Then There Were None* ☐

Same Difference

301. *Dressed to Kill* ☐
302. *Heaven Can Wait* (the 1978 version was a remake of *Here Comes Mr Jordan*, which starred Robert Montgomery) ☐
303. *Million Dollar Legs* ☐
304. *Monkey Business* ☐
305. *A Night to Remember* ☐
306. *Carrie* ☐
307. *The Turning Point* ☐
308. *Love Story* ☐
309. *Easy Come, Easy Go* (the second version was an Elvis Presley vehicle) ☐
310. *Till We Meet Again* ☐

State Of The Union

311. *Missouri* ☐
312. *Connecticut* ☐
313. *Oregon* ☐
314. *Virginia* ☐
315. *Wyoming* ☐
316. *Indiana* ☐
317. *California* ☐
318. *Oklahoma* ☐
319. *Tennessee* ☐
320. *California* ☐

Occupational Hazards

321. Claudette Colbert ☐

322. Robert de Niro ☐

323. Joan Crawford ☐

324. Bette Davis ☐

325. Otto Kruger ☐

326. Walter Pidgeon ☐

327. Barbara Stanwyck ☐

328. Dan Dailey ☐

329. Robert Redford ☐

330. Joe E. Brown ☐

The Not-So-Swinging Seventies

331. *The Girl from Petrovka*. Les Keyser called it 'an epic clinker' ☐

332. *The Swarm*. The *Guardian* said: 'You could pass it all off as a sick joke, except that it cost twelve million dollars, twenty-two million bees, and several years of someone's life.' ☐

333. *W. C. Fields and Me*. The 'me' was Carlotta Monti, Fields' mistress, who wrote the book on which some of the script was based. Judith Crist called it 'a stupid and pointless slander' ☐

334. *Brewster McCloud*. Pauline Kael in the *New Yorker* commented: 'The idea seems to be left over from a Victorian fable, but the style is like a Road Runner cartoon.' ☐

335. *Matilda*. The animal had to be played by a man in a skin, which was the crowning blow to any hopes the film had ☐

336. *The Cheap Detective*. Derek Malcolm thought there was enough talent in evidence for about twenty minutes on the Edinburgh Fringe ☐

337. *Sextette*. It was financed by two misguided millionaires, who did not get their money back ☐

338. *The White Buffalo*. The film was barely seen despite a cast including Kim Novak, Clint Walker, Jack Warden, Will Sampson, Stuart Whitman and John Carradine ☐

339. *The Sentinel*. Janet Maslin in *Newsweek* thought its gore made it 'a perfect film for those who like to slow down and look at traffic accidents' □

340. *The Sailor Who Fell From Grace With The Sea*. Benny Green thought it should be traded back to the Japs and made required viewing for timorous kamikaze pilots □

What's My Line?

341. *The Senator was Indiscreet* □

342. *The Nutty Professor* □

343. *Two Girls and a Sailor* □

344. *The Farmer's Daughter* or *The Ambassador's Daughter* □

345. *The Captain's Paradise* □

346. *Her Highness and the Bellboy* □

347. *The Emperor's Candlesticks* □

348. *Teacher's Pet* □

349. *Detective Story* □

350. *Judge Hardy's Children* □

Mixed Doubles

351–3. *Cattle Annie and Little Britches*: Diane Lane, Amanda Plummer □ □ □

354–6. *The Major and the Minor*: Ray Milland, Ginger Rogers □ □ □

357–9. *Molly and Me*: Gracie Fields, Monty Woolley □ □ □

360–62. *Me and Marlborough*: Cicely Courtneidge, Tom Walls □ □ □

363–5. *Gable and Lombard*: James Brolin, Jill Clayburgh □ □ □

366–8. *The Bachelor and the Bobbysoxer*: Cary Grant, Shirley Temple □ □ □

369–71. *Thunderbolt and Lightfoot*: Clint Eastwood, Jeff Bridges □ □ □

372–4. *Angel and the Badman*: Gail Russell, John Wayne □ □ □

375–7. *W. C. Fields and Me*: Rod Steiger, Valerie Perrine ☐ ☐ ☐

378–80. *The Great Scout and Cathouse Thursday*: Lee Marvin, Kay Lenz ☐ ☐ ☐

Dignity, Always Dignity

381–3. *History is Made at Night*; Charles Boyer, Jean Arthur ☐ ☐ ☐

384–6. *Twentieth Century*; John Barrymore, Carole Lombard ☐ ☐ ☐

387–9. *The Reformer and the Redhead*; Dick Powell, June Allyson ☐ ☐ ☐

390–92. *The Reincarnation of Peter Proud*; Michael Sarrazin, Jennifer O'Neill ☐ ☐ ☐

393–5. *Hotel Imperial*; Ray Milland, Isa Miranda ☐ ☐ ☐

396–8. *His Majesty O'Keefe*; Burt Lancaster, Joan Rice ☐ ☐ ☐

399–401. *The Impossible Years*; David Niven, Lola Albright ☐ ☐ ☐

402–4. *A Covenant with Death*; George Maharis, Katy Jurado ☐ ☐ ☐

405–7. *The Horizontal Lieutenant*; Jim Hutton, Paula Prentiss ☐ ☐ ☐

408–10. *The Notorious Landlady*; Jack Lemmon, Kim Novak ☐ ☐ ☐

World Gazetteer

411. *Jamaica Run* ☐

412. *Action in Arabia* ☐

413. *Carnival in Costa Rica* ☐

414. *Tanganyika* ☐

415. *An American Guerrilla in the Philippines* ☐

416. *Song of Russia* ☐

417. *Little Egypt* ☐

418. *High Road to China* ☐

419. *Secret Agent of Japan* ☐
420. *Masquerade in Mexico* ☐

Sleuths
421. Sam Spade ☐
422. Philip Marlowe ☐
423. Philo Vance ☐
424. Mike Hammer ☐
425. Inspector Maigret ☐
426. Hercule Poirot ☐
427. Miss Marple ☐
428. Nick Charles ☐
429. Inspector Clouseau ☐
430. Perry Mason ☐

A Rose By Any Other Name
431. True ☐
432. False (but she was in a TV drama called *All Passion Spent*) ☐
433. False, though it sounds likely ☐
434. True ☐
435. True ☐
436. True ☐
437. True ☐
438. True ☐
439. False: you may be thinking of *Attack of the Killer Tomatoes*, which was genuine ☐
440. True ☐

The Bad And The Ugly
441. Oliver Reed ☐
442. Tom Tyler ☐

443. Lon Chaney Jnr (and/or his stunt man Eddie Parker, with Tom Tyler in the flashbacks) ☐
444. Francis Lederer ☐
445. Lon Chaney Jnr ☐
446. Ricou Browning ☐
447. James Arness ☐
448. John Howard ☐
449. Vincent Price ☐
450. Henry Hull ☐

There's Always a First Time

451. Cary Grant ☐
452. Rock Hudson ☐
453. Richard Burton ☐
454. Sydney Greenstreet ☐
455. Kirk Douglas ☐
456. Vincent Price ☐
457. Paul Newman ☐
458. Walter Matthau ☐
459. Jean Simmons ☐
460. Fred Astaire ☐

Modern Types

461. Daniel Massey ☐
462. Alan Arkin ☐
463. Alec Guinness ☐
464. Walter Pidgeon ☐
465. Alexander Knox ☐
466. James Stewart ☐
467. Simon Ward ☐
468. John Mills ☐

469. Robert Walker ☐
470. Curt Jurgens ☐

The Previous Time Around

471–2. *Gunga Din*: Sam Jaffe ☐ ☐
473–4. *House of Strangers*: Edward G. Robinson ☐ ☐
475–6. *Kiss of Death*: Richard Widmark ☐ ☐
477–8. *The Sea Wolf*: Edward G. Robinson ☐ ☐
479–80. *The Letter*: Bette Davis ☐ ☐
481–2. *It Started With Eve*: Charles Laughton ☐ ☐
483–4. *Mad About Music*: Herbert Marshall ☐ ☐
485–6. *Boudu Saved from Drowning*: Michel Simon ☐ ☐
487–8. *Red Dust*: Jean Harlow. (*Congo Maisie* was an even closer approximation to the original.) ☐ ☐
489–90. *Strangers on a Train*: Robert Walker ☐ ☐
491–2. *Swamp Water*: Walter Brennan (yes, he played the role twice) ☐ ☐
493–4. *Son of Fury*: Tyrone Power ☐ ☐
495–6. *The More the Merrier*: Charles Coburn ☐ ☐
497–8. *The Man Who Played God*: George Arliss ☐ ☐
499–500. *The Man in Half Moon Street*: Nils Asther ☐ ☐
501–2. *The Shop Around the Corner*: Margaret Sullavan ☐ ☐
503–4. *Love Affair*: Irene Dunne ☐ ☐
505–6. *Whoopee*: Eddie Cantor ☐ ☐
507–8. *The Paleface*: Bob Hope ☐ ☐
509–10. *Ruggles of Red Gap*: Charles Laughton ☐ ☐

Run For Your Life

511. Trevor Howard ☐
512. Robert Redford ☐
513. Robert Cummings ☐
514. Kenneth More ☐

515. Derek Farr ☐

516. Gregory Peck ☐

517. Paul Newman ☐

518. Bob Hope ☐

519. Derrick de Marney ☐

520. Ann Sheridan ☐

Hollywood At War

521–3. *Escape*. Nazimova. Ethel Vance ☐ ☐ ☐

524–6. *Man Hunt*. Fritz Lang. *Rogue Male* ☐ ☐ ☐

527–9. *Caught in the Draft*. Dorothy Lamour. Eddie Bracken ☐ ☐ ☐

530–32. *Dive Bomber*. Errol Flynn. Alexis Smith ☐ ☐ ☐

533–5. *A Yank in the R. A. F.*. Darryl F. Zanuck. The Evacuation of Dunkirk ☐ ☐ ☐

536–8. *To Be or Not To Be*. Sig Rumann. Charles Durning ☐ ☐ ☐

539–41. *Joe Smith, American*. Robert Young. By being blindfolded again and remembering the sounds he heard the first time ☐ ☐ ☐

542–4. *Saboteur*. In the torch of the Statue of Liberty. The sinking of the *Normandie* in New York Harbour ☐ ☐ ☐

545–7. *Mrs Miniver*. The Evacuation of Dunkirk. He married the star, Greer Garson ☐ ☐ ☐

548–50. *Casablanca. Everybody Comes to Rick's*. Ronald Reagan ☐ ☐ ☐

551–3. The assassination of the Nazi Heydrich by Czech patriots. *The Silent Village. Edge of Darkness* ☐ ☐ ☐

554–6. *So Proudly We Hail*. Veronica Lake. Mark Sandrich ☐ ☐ ☐

557–9. *Guadalcanal Diary. Wake Island. Sands of Iwo Jima* ☐ ☐ ☐

560–62. Alfred Hitchcock. *Lifeboat. Rope* ☐ ☐ ☐

563–5. *The Hitler Gang. The Paleface. Singin' in the Rain*: Gene Kelly and Donald O'Connor danced rings around him ☐ ☐ ☐

566–8. *Since You Went Away*. Joseph Cotten. Monty Woolley
□ □ □

569–70. *The Best Years of Our Lives*. Cathy O'Donnell □ □

It Must Stand For Something

571. DEAD ON ARRIVAL: a police abbreviation. The hero was dead to all effect: though he spent the next twenty-four hours looking for the culprit, he had been fatally poisoned □

572. REVOLUTIONS PER MINUTE: a familiar abbreviation from gramophone records was applied to student protest □

573. OFFICE OF STRATEGIC SERVICES: the wartime predecessor of the CIA □

574. ZERO POPULATION GROWTH: a description of the state of a future society □

575. MOBILE ARMY SURGICAL HOSPITAL □

576. THE DRILL INSTRUCTOR □

577. SITUATION NORMAL, ALL FOULED UP. That was the polite version: American soldiers used a different word beginning with F. The 1945 film played in Britain as *Welcome Home* □

578. Not, as many people thought, son of a bitch, but explained in the film as STANDARD OPERATIONAL BULLSHIT □

579. In World War II, everybody knew that these familiar initials applied to the American forces, but few could translate them as GOVERNMENT ISSUE □

580. This Anglo-German adventure film of 1933 was about giant aircraft bases which amounted to islands in the sea, or FLOATING PLATFORMS □

City Streets

581. Hollywood □

582. Las Vegas □

583. Phoenix City □

584. Springfield ☐

585. Indianapolis ☐

586. San Francisco ☐

587. Chicago ☐

588. Miami ☐

589. Cincinnati ☐

590. Philadelphia ☐

Catchphrase

591. Arthur Askey ☐

592. Sid Field ☐

593. Tommy Trinder (who appeared in a dreadful film under this title) ☐

594. Frank Randle ☐

595. Max Miller (who might add: 'When I'm dead and gone, that's it!') ☐

596. Oliver Hardy, after being on the receiving end of some act of crass stupidity by Stan ☐

597. Jimmy Durante ☐

598. W. C. Fields (it was the nearest he could get to 'God damn!') ☐

599. Joan Davis, especially in *Show Business* ☐

600. Mr Magoo. Jim Backus actually said it only once on his behalf, in *Fuddy Duddy Buddy*, but it's a lovely line ☐

One-Shots

601. *At Long Last Love* (1975), Peter Bogdanovich's flop musical ☐

602. *The Legend of the Lone Ranger* (1981), Lew Grade's flop Western ☐

603. *Homicidal* (1961): nobody really knew whether Jean, who played a transvestite, was he, she or it ☐

604. *The Jazz Singer* (1980): it didn't do for his film career what a previous version had done for Jolson's ☐

605. *Saturday Night Fever* (1978): whatever happened to her? ☐

606. *The Last Tycoon* (1976): South Africa presumably welcomed her back ☐

607. *An American in Paris* (1951): MGM made no further offers ☐

608. *Guess Who's Coming to Dinner* (1967): she only did it to please her aunt, Katharine Hepburn ☐

609. *Melba* (1953): the diva went on singing, but not on screen ☐

610. *Once In a Blue Moon* (1934): the New York comic went back on the Chief ☐

One-Two Shots

611. Miliza Korjus ('rhymes with gorgeous') ☐
612. James Baskett: he died the year the film was released ☐
613. Michael North ☐
614. Christine Carere ☐
615. Bella Darvi ☐
616. Edward Woods ☐
617. Taina Elg ☐
618. Bekim Fehmiu ☐
619. Sigrid Gurie ☐
620. Stathis Giallelis ☐

Laurence Olivier

621. *The Demi-Paradise* ☐
622. *The Devil's Disciple* ☐
623. *Term of Trial* ☐
624. *Q Planes* (US: *Clouds Over Europe*) ☐
625. *Potiphar's Wife* ☐

626. *Fire Over England* ☐
627. *Conquest of the Air* ☐
628. *The Temporary Widow* ☐
629. *Moscow Nights* ☐
630. *The Betsy* ☐

Very Important People

631. *Young Winston* (1972) ☐
632. *Sunrise at Campobello* (1960) ☐
633. *Magnificent Doll* (1946) ☐
634. *If I Were King* (1938) ☐
635. *The Hunchback of Notre Dame* (1939) ☐
636. *Nell Gwyn* (1935) ☐
637. *Cromwell* (1970) ☐
638. *Wilson* (1944) ☐
639. *Lady Caroline Lamb* (1972) ☐
640. *Compulsion* (1959) ☐
641. *The Young Mr Pitt* (1942) ☐
642. *Captain Boycott* (1947: a cameo role) ☐
643. *Oh What a Lovely War* (1969) ☐
644. *The Spirit of St Louis* (1957) ☐
645. *The Prime Minister* (1940) ☐
646. *Anne of the Thousand Days* (1969) ☐
647. *A Man For All Seasons* (1967) ☐
648. *The Story of Mankind* (1957) ☐
649. *The Mudlark* (1950) ☐
650. *Fire Over England* (1937) ☐

Graham Greenery

651. *Confidential Agent* ☐
652. *England Made Me* ☐

653. *Brighton Rock*: he made a record telling her he despised her, but the needle got stuck ☐

654. *The Green Cockatoo* ☐

655. *21 Days* ☐

656. Rod Steiger ☐

657. *Loser Takes All* ☐

658. *A Gun For Sale* ☐

659. *The Man Within* ☐

660. *The Quiet American*: the star was Michael Redgrave ☐

Hey, Mister!

661. *The Great Mr Handel*, with Wilfrid Lawson ☐

662. *Mr Winkle Goes to War*, with Edward G. Robinson ☐

663. *Mr Majesty*, with Charles Bronson ☐

664. *Mr Sardonicus*, with Guy Rolfe ☐

665. *Mister Buddwing*, with James Garner ☐

666. *Mr Lucky*, with Cary Grant ☐

667. *Mr Imperium*, with Ezio Pinza ☐

668. *Call Me Mister*, with Dan Dailey and Betty Grable ☐

669. *They Call Me Mister Tibbs*, with Sidney Poitier ☐

670. *Mister 880*, with Edmund Gwenn ☐

Brush up Your Shakespeare

671. *The Taming of the Shrew* (1929) ☐

672. *The Boys From Syracuse* (1940, based on *A Comedy of Errors*) ☐

673. *Macbeth*, as *Joe Macbeth* (1955) ☐

674. *Forbidden Planet* ☐

675. *Othello* ☐

676. *King Lear* ☐

677. *Macbeth* ☐

678. *Julius Caesar* ☐

156

679. The nurse in *Romeo and Juliet* (1936, 1954 and 1968) ☐

680. *A Midsummer Night's Dream* (1935) ☐

Frank Capra's People

681–3. Loretta Young. Jean Harlow. Robert Williams ☐ ☐ ☐

684–5. Gavin Gordon. Nils Asther ☐ ☐

686–9. May Robson. Bette Davis. Edward Everett Horton.
Pocketful of Miracles ☐ ☐ ☐ ☐

690–93. Jameson Thomas. Walter Connolly. Roscoe Karns.
Blankets slung over a washing-line to give the heroine some
privacy in the motel ☐ ☐ ☐ ☐

694–5. A horse. *Riding High* ☐ ☐

696–9. Margaret Seddon. 'Pixilated'. H. B. Warner. Raymond
Walburn ☐ ☐ ☐ ☐

700–703. Isabel Jewell. They became brothers. Jane Wyatt. Sam
Jaffe ☐ ☐ ☐ ☐

704–5. Jean Arthur. Harry Carey ☐ ☐

706–8. Josephine Hull and Jean Adair. John Alexander ☐ ☐ ☐

709–10. An angel. Lionel Barrymore ☐ ☐

Cherchez La Femme

711. Patrice Wymore ☐

712. Virginia Gilmore ☐

713. Janet Blair ☐

714. Betty Field ☐

715. Anna Lee ☐

716. Carroll Baker ☐

717. Genevieve Page ☐

718. Priscilla Lane ☐

719. Irene Manning ☐

720. Edwige Feuillere ☐

721. Judy Tyler ☐

722. Laraine Day ☐
723. Felicia Farr ☐
724. Betty Field ☐
725. Gloria Grahame ☐
726. Lee Remick ☐
727. Rosemary Lane ☐
728. Joan Caulfield ☐
729. Doris Davenport ☐
730. Virginia Leith ☐

Cherchez L'Homme

731. James Davis, later of *Dallas* ☐
732. Michael O'Shea ☐
733. Charles Korvin ☐
734. David Farrar ☐
735. Lee Bowman ☐
736. Lowell Sherman ☐
737. Richard Johnson ☐
738. Alan Marshal ☐
739. Mark Stevens ☐
740. James Ellison ☐

A. K. A.

741. Edmund Gwenn: Mister 880 was a forger ☐
742. David Huddleston ☐
743. Will Hay ☐
744. Basil Rathbone ☐
745. Lionel Atwill ☐
746. Joan Collins ☐
747. James Coburn ☐
748. Katharine Hepburn ☐

749. Joan Crawford; the hussy was Peggy O'Neal, friend of Andrew Jackson ☐
750. Meryl Streep ☐
751. George Arliss ☐
752. Boris Karloff ☐
753. Roland Young ☐
754. Roger Moore ☐
755. James Cagney ☐
756. Leslie Howard ☐
757. Anthony Quinn ☐
758. Alan Ladd ☐
759. Bob Hope ☐
760. Gary Cooper, playing Lou Gehrig ☐

Sing As We Go

761. *Girl Crazy* ☐
762. *An American in Paris* ☐
763. *Bitter Sweet* ☐
764. *The Gay Divorcée* ☐
765. *A Damsel in Distress* ☐
766. *Destry Rides Again* ☐
767. *On the Avenue* ☐
768. *Rosalie* ☐
769. *Swing Time* ☐
770. *Roberta* ☐
771. *Naughty Marietta* ☐
772. *Rose Marie* ☐
773. *The Pirate* ☐
774. *Good News* ☐
775. *Till The Clouds Roll By* ☐
776. *Blue Skies* ☐

777. *Road to Singapore* ☐
778. *New Moon* ☐
779. *42nd Street* ☐
780. *Pinocchio* ☐
781. *Sing You Sinners* ☐
782. *Shall We Dance?* ☐
783. *Carefree* ☐
784. *Follow the Fleet* ☐
785. *Top Hat* ☐
786. *Hellzapoppin* ☐
787. *Yankee Doodle Dandy* ☐
788. *My Gal Sal* ☐
789. *The Jolson Story* ☐
790. *Centennial Summer* ☐
791. *Night and Day* ☐
792. *Ziegfeld Follies* ☐
793. *The Harvey Girls* ☐
794. *Holiday Inn* ☐
795. *Road to Morocco* ☐
796. *Star Spangled Rhythm* ☐
797. *You Were Never Lovelier* ☐
798. *Hello Frisco, Hello* ☐
799. *State Fair* ☐
800. *Meet Me in St Louis* ☐
801. *Going My Way* ☐
802. *Cabin in the Sky* ☐
803. *Show Business* ☐
804. *Cover Girl* ☐
805. *Higher and Higher* ☐
806. *The Gang's All Here* ☐
807. *Thank Your Lucky Stars* ☐
808. *Easter Parade* ☐

809. *Words and Music* ☐
810. *Damn Yankees* ☐
811. *The Pajama Game* ☐
812. *Pal Joey* ☐
813. *Funny Face* ☐
814. *The King and I* ☐
815. *High Society* ☐
816. *Oklahoma!* ☐
817. *Kismet* ☐
818. *On the Riviera* ☐
819. *On the Town* ☐
820. *The Barkleys of Broadway* ☐
821. *Singin' in the Rain* ☐
822. *Take Me Out to the Ball Game* ☐
823. *Hans Christian Andersen* ☐
824. *Call Me Madam* ☐
825. *Kiss Me Kate* ☐
826. *The Band Wagon* ☐
827. *Annie Get Your Gun* ☐
828. *Calamity Jane* ☐
829. *Red Garters* ☐
830. *Daddy Long Legs* ☐
831. *Guys and Dolls* ☐
832. *Seven Brides for Seven Brothers* ☐
833. *Brigadoon* ☐
834. *There's No Business Like Show Business* ☐
835. *It's Always Fair Weather* ☐
836. *The Music Man* ☐
837. *Camelot* ☐
838. *Gypsy* ☐
839. *Mary Poppins* ☐
840. *The Sound of Music* ☐

City Of My Dreams

841. *Timbuktu* ☐
842. *Algiers* ☐
843. *Benghazi* ☐
844. *Lisbon* ☐
845. *San Francisco* ☐
846. *Istanbul* ☐
847. *Cairo* ☐
848. *Rio* ☐
849. *Cairo* (different story) ☐
850. *Calcutta* ☐

My Story

851. Tyrone Power ☐
852. Sal Mineo ☐
853. William Bendix ☐
854. Ray Danton ☐
855. Donald O'Connor ☐
856. Gary Busey ☐
857. Keefe Brasselle ☐
858. Will Rogers Jnr ☐
859. Kathryn Grayson ☐
860. Ann Blyth ☐
861. Bob Hope ☐
862. Van Heflin ☐
863. Debbie Reynolds ☐
864. Kim Novak ☐
865. Patrice Munsel ☐
866. George Arliss ☐
867. John Gielgud ☐
868. Sarah Miles ☐

869. George Hamilton □

870. Douglas 'Wrong Way' Corrigan, the American aviator who set out to fly cross country but ended up on the far side of the Atlantic. He was no better at acting than at navigation □

The Haunted House Of Hammer

871–2. John Richardson: *The Vengeance of She* □ □

873–41. John Carson: *The Plague of the Zombies* □ □

875–6. Noel Willman: *Kiss of the Vampire* □ □

877–8. Freda Jackson: *The Brides of Dracula* □ □

879–80. Barbara Shelley: *The Gorgon* (whether Miss Shelley actually *played* the gorgon is open to doubt) □ □

881–2. Terence Morgan: *The Curse of the Mummy's Tomb* □ □

883–4. Jennifer Pearce: *The Reptile* □ □

885–6. Anton Diffring: *The Man Who Could Cheat Death* □ □

887–8. Freddie Jones: *Frankenstein Must Be Destroyed* □ □

889–90. Ingrid Pitt: *The Vampire Lovers* □ □

The Hammer Ladies

891. *The Viking Queen* (1967) □

892. *The Mummy's Shroud* (1967) □

893. *The Vengeance of She* (1968) □

894. *The Curse of the Mummy's Tomb* (1964) □

895. *The Brides of Dracula* (1960) □

896. *Frankenstein Created Woman* (1967) □

897. *Dracula Has Risen from the Grave* (1968) □

898. *When Dinosaurs Ruled the Earth* (1970) □

899. *Creatures the World Forgot* (1971) □

890. *Slave Girls* (1968) □

Black-Hearted Men

901–2. Gert Frobe in *Goldfinger* □ □

903–4. Roy Emerton, he of the long nose and cross-eyes, in *Lorna Doone* □ □

905–6. Marlon Brando played Henry James' evil ghost in *The Nightcomers* □ □

907–8. Laurence Olivier in *The Seven Per Cent Solution* □ □

909–10. Melville Cooper in *The Adventures of Robin Hood* □ □

911–12. Victor Jory in *The Adventures of Tom Sawyer* □ □

913–14. Roland Young in *David Copperfield* □ □

915–16. Robert Newton (born for the part) in *Oliver Twist* □ □

917–18. Cedric Hardwicke in *Nicholas Nickleby* □ □

919–20. Tod Slaughter, the great lipsmacker, in *Sweeney Todd* □ □

921–2. Sydney Greenstreet in *The Woman in White* □ □

923–4. Tod Slaughter again, in *The Face at the Window* □ □

925–6. Cedric Hardwicke in *The Hunchback of Notre Dame* □ □

927–8. Basil Rathbone in *A Tale of Two Cities* □ □

929–30. Henry Oscar in *The Return of the Scarlet Pimpernel* □ □

931–2. John Barrymore in *Svengali* □ □

933–4. Boris Karloff in *The Mask of Fu Manchu* □ □

935–6. Raymond Massey in *The Prisoner of Zenda* □ □

937–8. Robert Newton ('Aye, Jim lad') in *Treasure Island* □ □

939–40. Keir Dullea in *De Sade* □ □

It Happened This Way

941. *A Woman's Face* (1941) □

942. *Casablanca* (1942) □

943. *War and Peace* (1956) □

944. *Queen Christina* (1933) □

945. *The Sea of Grass* (1947) □

946. *Never Steal Anything Small* (1959) □

947. *It Happened One Night* (1934) □
948. *Dial M for Murder* (1954) □
949. *Pinky* (1949) □
950. *The Pride and the Passion* (1957) □

Not All My Own Work
951. Nathanael West □
952. Maxwell Anderson □
953. William Faulkner □
954. Dashiell Hammett □
955. Aldous Huxley □
956. Christopher Isherwood □
957. S. J. Perelman □
958. Raymond Chandler □
959. F. Scott Fitzgerald □
960. Lillian Hellman □

Name and Address
961. Alan Ladd □
962. Gary Cooper □
963. Edward G. Robinson □
964. Gordon Harker □
965. James Cagney □
966. Edmund O'Brien □
967. Louis Jouvet □
968. Charles Laughton □
969. Vincent Price □
970. Tyrone Power □

Pictorial Quiz: Find The Title

971. *Lure of the Wilderness* ☐

972. Howard Hughes ☐

973. *King of Kings* ☐

974. *To Have and Have Not* ☐

975. *The Pleasure Seekers* ☐

976. *Mad Wednesday*: there was another version called *The Sin of Harold Diddlebock* ☐

977. *Professor Beware* ☐

978. *Mr Deeds Goes to Town* ☐

979. *Unfaithfully Yours* ☐

980. *Never Give a Sucker an Even Break* ☐

981. *The Killer Elite* ☐

982. *Invasion of the Body Snatchers* ☐

983. *The Gambler* ☐

984. Eisenhower, in *Ike* ☐

985. *They Shoot Horses, Don't They?* ☐

986. *The Damned Don't Cry* ☐

987. *Mildred Pierce* ☐

988. *Intruder in the Dust* ☐

989. *Storm Warning* ☐

990. *Old Acquaintance, Mrs Skeffington* ☐

991. *Death of a Gunfighter* ☐

992. *Kiss of Death* ☐

993. *Stormy Weather* ☐

994. Archie Bunker in *All in the Family* ☐

995. He doesn't exist, but the name has been used when there is a controversy about the direction. In this case Don Siegel and Robert Totten are said to have shared the burden ☐

996. *Three Young Texans* ☐

997. *South Pacific* ☐

998. Eddie Cantor in *The Eddie Cantor Story* ☐

999. A television producer (*Charlie's Angels*, etc) ☐

1000. *Journey to the Centre of the Earth* ☐

1001. *Every Day's a Holiday* ☐

1002. Victor McLaglen ☐

1003. *Night After Night* ☐

1004. Al Shean, the original partner in the Gallacher and Shean duo; Winninger played Gallagher ☐

1005. *Bringing Up Baby* ☐

1006. *Boom!* ☐

1007. *The Driver's Seat* ☐

1008. *The Last Days of Dolwyn* ☐

1009. *The Scoundrel* ☐

1010. *The Intimate Stranger*, also known as *Finger of Guilt* ☐

1011. *Shoot Out* ☐

1012. *Days of Glory* ☐

1013. Martha Hyer ☐

1014. *Peter Ibbetson* ☐

1015. *Duel in the Sun* ☐

1016. *Track of the Cat* ☐

1017. *The Night of the Hunter* ☐

1018. *The Little Foxes* ☐

1019. *The Light That Failed* ☐

1020. *The Miracle of Morgan's Creek* ☐

1021. *The Laughing Policeman* (in the UK, *An Investigation of Murder*) ☐

1022. *The Fortune Cookie* (in the UK, *Meet Whiplash Willie*) ☐

1023. *Hush . . . Hush, Sweet Charlotte* ☐

1024. *An Officer and a Gentleman* ☐

1025. *Cool Hand Luke* ☐

1026. *Scandal Sheet* ☐

1027. *All the King's Men* ☐

1028. Helen Broderick ☐

1029. *From Here to Eternity* □

1030. *Rogues of Sherwood Forest* □

1031. *Take a Hard Ride* □

1032. *100 Rifles* □

1033. *The Good, the Bad and the Ugly* □

1034. *Lady in the Dark* □

1035. *Night of the Demon* (in US, *Curse of the Demon*) □

1036. *Judith* □

1037. *Two Women* □

1038. *Father Brown* □

1039. *Front Page Story* □

1040. *Come Back Little Sheba* □

Split Personalities

1041–2. They all played the yellow peril, Dr Fu Manchu: Sellers in one of his last unhappy vehicles, *The Fiendish Plot of Fu Manchu* □ □

1043. They all played Rudolf Rassendyll in versions of *The Prisoner of Zenda* □

1044. They all played the French jewel thief Arsène Lupin: Barrymore in 1932 (*Arsène Lupin*), Douglas in 1937 (*Arsène Lupin Returns*) and Korvin in 1944 (*Enter Arsène Lupin*) □

1045–8. They all played the Roman emperor Nero: Laughton in *The Sign of the Cross*, Ustinov in *Quo Vadis?* and Lorre (briefly) in *The Story of Mankind* □ □ □ □

1049–40. They all played Charlie Chan: Winters at the tag-end of the original series, Martin on TV, and Ustinov in the dreary *Charlie Chan and the Curse of the Dragon Queen* (1981) □ □

1051. They all played Bulldog Drummond (in the thirties) □

1052. They all played the Cisco Kid □

1053. They all played Ellery Queen □

1054–6. They all played the Invisible Man: Price in *The Invisible Man Returns* (1939), Hall in two forties episodes, and Franz in *Abbott and Costello Meet the Invisible Man* (1951) □ □ □

1057–60. They all played Mickey Spillane's tough detective Mike Hammer: Elliott in *I the Jury* (1953), Assante in the 1982 remake, and Meeker in *Kiss Me Deadly* □ □ □ □

Who Wrote the Book?

1061. Dashiell Hammett □

1062. Daphne du Maurier □

1063. Lloyd C. Douglas □

1064. Olive Higgins Prouty □

1065. Arthur Hailey □

1066. Lloyd C. Douglas □

1067. Bram Stoker □

1068. Anthony Hope □

1069. J. B. Priestley (British title: *Benighted*) □

1070. Henryk Sienkiewicz (approximate spelling allowed) □

1071. Niven Busch □

1072. Lew Wallace □

1073. Owen Wister □

1074. P. C. Wren □

1075. W. Somerset Maugham □

1076. James Hilton □

1077. John Buchan □

1078. Wilkie Collins □

1079. Rafael Sabatini □

1080. Eric Hodgin □

Author! Author!

1081. Philip Barry (second version as *High Society*) □

1082. Arthur Conan Doyle □

1083. Mary Roberts Rinehart □

1084. James Hilton □

1085. Alice Hegan Rice □

1086. John Willard □

1087. A. E. W. Mason □

1088. Ethel Lina White (original title *The Wheel Spins*) □

1089. Gaston Leroux □

1090. Leo Tolstoy □

1091. James Hilton □

1092. L. Frank Baum □

1093. Fannie Hurst □

1094. Ethel Lina White again (original title *Some Must Watch*) □

1095. Tennessee Williams □

1096. Patrick Hamilton (play known in US as *Angel Street*) □

1097. Ben Hecht and Charles MacArthur □

1098. Fyodor Dostoievsky □

1099. Maurice Maeterlinck □

1100. Emlyn Williams □

Include Me Out

1101. '10'. Segal no doubt came to regret his 'creative differences' □

1102. *David Copperfield* (1935). Laughton was unhappy as Micawber and walked off, recommending Fields □

1103. *Annie Get Your Gun.* Garland was so difficult that she was fired □

1104. *Kiss Me Stupid.* Sellers had had the first of his heart attacks □

1105. *Easter Parade.* Kelly had a leg injury □

1106. *Captain Blood.* Donat was unhappy in Hollywood and went back home □

1107. *Queen Christina.* Garbo wanted to give another chance to her former lover □

1108. *Hush Hush Sweet Charlotte.* The double act from *Whatever Happened to Baby Jane?* had been reassembled, but Crawford fell ill and could not recover in time □

1109. *Casablanca*. The production had originally been set as a minor Reagan vehicle called *Everybody Comes to Rick's* □

1110. *Doctor Doolittle*. Tricky. Harrison had begun work and then refused to continue; Plummer was contracted to replace him. Harrison then came back, and Fox paid off Plummer □

Creature Features

1111. Henry Hull □

1112. He suffered from the distorting disease acromegaly, so that he looked frightening without any make-up □

1113. *The Brides of Dracula* (1960) □

1114. David Peel, of whom little was heard thereafter □

1115. Tom Tyler (with flashback inserts of Boris Karloff from *The Mummy*) □

1116. Not Bela Lugosi, who played the monster. The only actual Frankenstein on view was Ilona Massey □

1117. O. B. Clarence, the gentle stage actor who later played the Aged P in *Great Expectations* □

1118. George M. Cohan's *Seven Keys to Baldpate* □

1119. In Westminster Abbey □

1120. *The Creature from the Black Lagoon* □

The Common Touch

1121. They were all directed by well-known actors, who did not however appear: Dick Powell, Jack Lemmon, Paul Newman □

1122. They all had scenes involving airships which came to grief □

1123. The heroes all suffered from amnesia: Ronald Colman, Gregory Peck, James Garner □

1124. They all involved historical assassinations: Gandhi, Archduke Ferdinand, Julius Caesar □

1125. The titles were all names of motor cars □

1126. All concerned anti-Semitism □

1127. A principal character played an angel from Heaven: Cary Grant, Jack Benny, James Mason □

1128. All were set in Berlin □

1129. A dog was a leading character □

1130. All concerned attempted assassinations □

1131. All had ballet as a background □

1132. All had baseball as a background □

1133. Abortion played a part in the plot □

1134. All were directed by the leading actor in each case: Albert Finney, Robert Montgomery, Clive Brook □

1135. All had advertising as a background □

1136. All partly concerned an air balloon □

1137. All climaxed at the Alamo □

1138. A leading character was a dipsomaniac: David Farrar, Bing Crosby, Ingrid Bergman □

1139. All the parts shown were played by moonlighting authors: Compton Mackenzie, Hugh Walpole, Alexander Woollcott □

1140. All are books written by actors: David Niven, Dirk Bogarde, Ruth Chatterton □

Sherlock Holmes

1141. Reginald Denny □

1142. *His Last Bow*. Rathbone's final patriotic speech was a direct quote □

1143. A book of matches □

1144. Henry Daniell □

1145. André Morell □

1146. *Crazy House*, which was set in Universal Studios □

1147. *The Triumph of Sherlock Holmes* □

1148. Roger Moore, certainly the worst Holmes of all □

1149. A small garden fork □

1150. James Mason □

Tinseltown

1151. *Once in a Lifetime* (1933) □

1152. *A Star is Born* (1937) □

1153. *The Goldwyn Follies* (1938) □

1154. *Stand-in* (1937) □

1155. *World Première* (1941) □

1156. *Boy Meets Girl* (1938). (The use of the term supervisor denotes it as a Warner film.) □

1157. *Dreamboat* (1952) □

1158. *Star Spangled Rhythm* (1942) (The character name was remarkably similar to that of Paramount's then production chief B. G. DeSylva.) □

1159. *In a Lonely Place* (1949) □

1160. *The Legend of Lylah Clare* (1968) □

Best Actors

1161–2. Gary Cooper: *Sergeant York* □ □

1163–4. Victor McLaglen: *The Informer* □ □

1165–6. James Stewart: *The Philadelphia Story* □ □

1167–8. Ronald Colman: *A Double Life* □ □

1169–70. Peter Finch: *Network* □ □

1171–2. Ernest Borgnine: *Marty* □ □

1173–4. Cliff Robertson: *Charley* □ □

1175–6. George Arliss: *Disraeli* □ □

1177–8. Fredric March: *The Best Years of Our Lives* □ □

1179–80. James Cagney: *Yankee Doodle Dandy* □ □

1181–2. Laurence Olivier: *Hamlet* □ □

1183–4. Wallace Berry: *The Champ* □ □

1185–6. Warner Baxter: *In Old Arizona* □ □

1187–8. Charles Laughton: *The Private Life of Henry VIII* □ □

1189–90. Art Carney: *Harry and Tonto* □ □

1191–2. Marlon Brando: *On the Waterfront* □ □

1193–4. Gene Hackman: *The French Connection* □ □

1195–6. Rex Harrison: *My Fair Lady* □ □

1197–8. Gary Cooper: *High Noon* □ □

1199–1200. Humphrey Bogart: *The African Queen* □ □

1201–2. Paul Muni: *The Life of Emile Zola* □ □

1203–4. Clark Gable: *It Happened One Night* □ □

1205–6. Robert Donat: *Goodbye Mr Chips* □ □

1207–8. Spencer Tracy: *Boys' Town* □ □

1209–10. Lionel Barrymore: *A Free Soul* □ □

Best Actresses

1211–12. Bette Davis: *Jezebel* □ □

1213–14. Greer Garson: *Mrs Miniver* □ □

1215–16. Joan Crawford: *Mildred Pierce* □ □

1217–18. Helen Hayes: *The Sin of Madelon Claudet* □ □

1219–20. Bette Davis: *Dangerous* □ □

1221–2. Jane Wyman: *Johnny Belinda* □ □

1223–4. Ellen Burstyn: *Alice Doesn't Live Here Any More* □ □

1225–6. Elizabeth Taylor: *Who's Afraid of Virginia Woolf?* □ □

1227–8. Audrey Hepburn: *Roman Holiday* □ □

1229–30. Julie Christie: *Darling* □ □

1231–2. Shirley Booth: *Come Back Little Sheba* □ □

1233–4. Vivien Leigh: *A Streetcar Named Desire* □ □

1235–6. Ingrid Bergman: *Anastasia* □ □

1237–8. Ingrid Bergman: *Gaslight* □ □

1239–40. Luise Rainer: *The Good Earth* □ □

1241–2. Katharine Hepburn: *Morning Glory* □ □

1243–4. Olivia de Havilland: *The Heiress* □ □

1245–6. Vivien Leigh: *Gone With The Wind* □ □

1247–8. Ginger Rogers: *Kitty Foyle* □ □

1249–50. Joan Fontaine: *Suspicion* □ □

1251–2. Luise Rainer: *The Great Ziegfeld* □ □

1253–4. Claudette Colbert: *It Happened One Night* □ □

1255–6. Judy Holliday: *Born Yesterday* □ □

1257–8. Joanne Woodward: *The Three Faces of Eve* □ □

1259–60. Elizabeth Taylor: *Butterfield 8* □ □

1261–2. Marie Dressler: *Min and Bill* □ □

1263–4. Liza Minnelli: *Cabaret* □ □

1265–6. Glenda Jackson: *A Touch of Class* □ □

1267–8. Katharine Hepburn: *The Lion in Winter* □ □

1269–70. Maggie Smith: *The Prime of Miss Jean Brodie* □ □

Colourful Titles

1271. A famous jewel which was stolen □

1272. A night club □

1273. Emeralds □

1274. The lamp fixed outside every British police station □

1275. The first wound received by a soldier in action □

1276. Another night club □

1277. The danger that post-war Vienna would succumb to Russian influence □

1278. An English inn □

1279. The statuette sought by criminals in *The Maltese Falcon*, of which *The Black Bird* was a spoof □

1280. Yet another night club □

Strength Of Character

1281. Arthur Lucan (whose 'daughter Kitty' was played by his termagant wife Kitty MacShane) □

1282. Warren William □

1283. Arthur Lake, friend of William Randolph Hearst □

1284. Dennis Hoey, former revue comedian and opera singer □

1285. Warren Mitchell □

1286. Percy Kilbride (after whose death one further film was made with Parker Fennelly) ☐

1287. Ann Sothern ☐

1288. Chester Morris ☐

1289. Warner Baxter ☐

1290. A trick question: the Whistler was never seen except as a shadow in the title sequence ☐

Crystal Balls

1291. *Alphaville* ☐

1292. *THX 1138* ☐

1293. *The Time Machine* ☐

1294. *Metropolis* ☐

1295. *Just Imagine* ☐

1296. *Things To Come* ☐

1297. *Fahrenheit 451* ☐

1298. *Soylent Green* ☐

1299. *Quintet* ☐

1300. *Rollerball* ☐

Dickens

1301. Hay Petrie ☐

1302. Magwitch in *Great Expectations* (1946 and 1974) ☐

1303. Peggotty in *David Copperfield* (1934 and 1969) ☐

1304. *Scrooge* (1951 and 1971) ☐

1305. *Dombey and Son* ☐

1306. *The Mystery of Edwin Drood* (1935). He played John Jasper ☐

1307. *Nicholas Nickleby* (1947). He was Ralph Nickleby ☐

1308. Pip in *Great Expectations* (1946) ☐

1309. David in *David Copperfield* (1934) ☐

1310. *Great Expectations* ☐

1311. *Scrooge* ☐

1312. Jean Cadell ☐

1313. Frank Lawton ☐

1314. Edna May Oliver ☐

1315. James Hayter (*Nicholas Nickleby* as the Cheeryble twins, *The Pickwick Papers* as Mr Pickwick) ☐

1316. *A Tale of Two Cities* ☐

1317. *Oliver Twist* ☐

1318. Richard Attenborough. He did, however, play Mr Tungay in the 1969 *David Copperfield* ☐

1319. *Great Expectations* (1946) as Herbert Pocket ☐

1320. Again the 1969 *David Copperfield*, in which he was Mr Dick ☐

My Life In Print

1321. Charles Bickford ☐

1322. Mickey Rooney ☐

1323. Edward G. Robinson ☐

1324. Leo Gorcey ☐

1325. Errol Flynn ☐

1326. Joan Collins ☐

1327. John Gielgud ☐

1328. Ray Milland ☐

1329. Brian Aherne ☐

1330. Jack Hawkins ☐

1331. George Sanders ☐

1332. Rudy Vallee ☐

1333. Stewart Granger ☐

1334. Shirley Maclaine ☐

1335. Omar Sharif ☐

1336. Vincent Price ☐

1337. Rosalind Russell ☐

1338. Anne Baxter ☐
1339. Lillian Gish ☐
1340. Ronald Reagan ☐

My Life In Pictures

1341. *With a Song in My Heart* ☐
1342. *I'll Cry Tomorrow* ☐
1343. *The Five Pennies* ☐
1344. *The Joker is Wild* ☐
1345. *The Seven Little Foys* (in which he danced with Bob Hope) ☐
1346. *So This Is Love* (In the UK, *The Grace Moore Story*) ☐
1347. *The I Don't Care Girl* ☐
1348. *Golden Girl* ☐
1349. *St Louis Blues* (1958) ☐
1350. *Night and Day* (except that he played Cole Porter's professor rather than his fellow student) ☐

States Of The Union

1351. *California* ☐
1352. *New Mexico* ☐
1353. *Arizona* ☐
1354. *In Old Arizona* ☐
1355. *Oklahoma!* ☐
1356. *Christmas in Connecticut* ☐
1357. *Hawaii* ☐
1358. *New York, New York* (the second New York is not mere repetition, but in the postal address denotes the state in which New York City is situated) ☐
1359. *Texas* ☐
1360. *Louisiana Purchase* ☐

It Takes Two to Tango

1361–2. Fred MacMurray and Claudette Colbert. All were comedies except the surprisingly gloomy *Maid of Salem*, which was made first ☐ ☐

1363–4. Wallace Beery and Marjorie Main ☐ ☐

1365–6. Dick Powell and Ruby Keeler, the winsom twosome of Warners' thirties musicals ☐ ☐

1367–8. Van Johnson and June Allyson, 'teenage' heart-throbs of the fifties ☐ ☐

1369–70. Clark Gable and Myrna Loy, the king and queen of MGM in the later thirties ☐ ☐

1371–2. Clark Gable and Joan Crawford, who had reigned as a duo at MGM from 1933 on ☐ ☐

1373–4. Dick Powell and Joan Blondell, who worked so well in double harness that they were married for a while ☐ ☐

1375–6. Joel McCrea and Barbara Stanwyck, thoroughgoing professionals both ☐ ☐

1377–8. Fred MacMurray and Madeleine Carroll, none of whose films together were at all memorable ☐ ☐

1379–80. Charles Farrell and Janet Gaynor, the perfect couple of the first talkies ☐ ☐

Hour of Glory

1381. George Zucco ☐

1382. Jane Darwell ☐

1383. Henry Travers ☐

1384. Cecil Kellaway ☐

1385. Melville Cooper ☐

1386. Sig Ruman ☐

1387. John Halliday ☐

1388. Steve Geray ☐

1389. Maria Ouspenskaya ☐

1390. Mildred Natwick ☐

1391. Laird Cregar ☐

1392. John Williams ☐

1393. Felix Bressart ☐

1394. Elizabeth Patterson ☐

1395. Florence Bates ☐

1396. Margaret Wycherly ☐

1397. Elisha Cook Jnr ☐

1398. Edward Van Sloan ☐

1399. Harry Davenport ☐

1400. Everett Sloane ☐

Keep It in the Family

1401. Charles and Geraldine Chaplin ☐

1402. Edgar and Candice Bergen ☐

1403. Lon Chaney and Lon Chaney Jnr ☐

1404. Errol and Sean Flynn ☐

1405. Michael and Vanessa Redgrave ☐

1406. John and Hayley Mills. (John also produced and directed *Sky West and Crooked* – or *Gypsy Girl* as it was known in the US.) ☐

1407. Robert and Alan Alda ☐

1408. Kirk and Michael Douglas ☐

1409. Ed and Keenan Wynn ☐

1410. John Barrymore and John Barrymore Jnr ☐

Step Into My Shoes

1411–13. *The Sea Wolf* (1940). The Raymond Massey version was called *Barricade*, and took place on dry land; the Barry Sullivan version was *Wolf Larsen* ☐ ☐ ☐

1414.15 *Waterloo Bridge* (1931). The John Kerr version was *Gaby* ☐ ☐

1416. *Showboat* (1929) ☐

1417. *A Star is Born* (1937) ☐

1418–19. *Dr Jekyll and Mr Hyde* (1931). The Paul Massie version was *The Two Faces of Dr Jekyll*, or in the US *House of Fright* ☐ ☐

1420–21. *The Maltese Falcon* (1931). The middle version was called *Satan Met a Lady* ☐ ☐

1422–4. *Red Dust* (1932). The Ann Sothern version was *Maisie*, the Ava Gardner version *Mogambo* ☐ ☐ ☐

1425–7. *The Most Dangerous Game* (1932); in the UK, *The Hounds of Zaroff*. The John Loder version was *A Game of Death*, the Richard Widmark version *Run for the Sun* ☐ ☐ ☐

1428–9. *The Last of Mrs Cheyney* (1929). The Garson version was *The Law and the Lady* ☐ ☐

1430. *The Three Musketeers* (1935) ☐

Forever Ealing

1431. *The Captive Heart*, first of the prisoner-of-war films. Michael Redgrave led the cast as a man who escaped with another man's identity ☐

1432. *Pool of London*. T. E. B. Clarke was the writer who hauled back his share of the script and rebuilt it into *The Lavender Hill Mob* ☐

1433. *It Always Rains on Sunday*, with Googie Withers and John McCallum on the wrong side of the law, opposed by Jack Warner as the detective. It has been suggested that *Passport to Pimlico* originated as a spoof on this somewhat heavy-going film ☐

1434. *The Blue Lamp*. Jack Warner's character, P. C. Dixon, was killed off after half an hour, but the image of the kindly bobby had been established and he was resurrected for BBC's *Dixon of Dock Green* ☐

1435. *The Goose Steps Out*; not the best of Hay's Ealing films, in which he strove to appear solo. He was more successful when accompanied by Claude Hulbert in *The Ghost of St Michael's* and *My Learned Friend* ☐

1436. *The Halfway House*, based on Denis Ogden's play *The*

Peaceful Inn, also starred Francoise Rosay, who from the middle of the war performed as often in British as in French films: *Johnny Frenchman* was another one for Ealing □

1437. Considering that *Dead of Night* had already shown the way, *Train of Events* was a surprising dud from a studio which had seemed able to handle short story composites. Whoever thought that trains were an infallible background was obviously wrong, even with a cast which included Valerie Hobson and John Clements □

1438. *Saraband for Dead Lovers*, from the novel by Helen Simpson; with Francoise Rosay, Flora Robson, and Peter Bull as the revolting Elector of Hanover. The Americans cut down the title to *Saraband*, but it didn't help business □

1439. *The Lavender Hill Mob* is almost too obvious from the merest clue. For the record, the mob consisted of Alec Guinness, Stanley Holloway, Sidney James and Alfie Bass □

1440. *Eureka Stockade* fared very little better when it was remade in the eighties as a television mini-series. It seems there are some stories the public just doesn't want to hear □

Titled Ladies

1441. Joyce Reynolds. Joyce who? you may say, but the film was popular enough to warrant a sequel, *Janie Gets Married* □

1442. Angie Dickinson □

1443. Lana Turner. She was on the way down rather than up □

1444. Anna Sten, whose Hollywood career was a misfire despite all the efforts of Sam Goldwyn's publicity machine □

1445. Spring Byington, then in her sixties; this was a comedy of old folk, with Ronald Reagan for juvenile lead □

1436. Pier Angeli □

1447. Elizabeth Taylor. This overlong study of teenage problems can hardly be said to have advanced her career □

1448. Loretta Young □

1449. Joan Fontaine, whose portrayal of a compulsive Victorian murderess was not among her better efforts □

1450. Shelley Winters. The film was a partial remake of *Destry Rides Again*, in which Marlene Dietrich had made such a hit, but the Winters version was only an also-ran ☐

Titled Gents

1451. Johnny Mack Brown. Robert Taylor was in the 1940 remake ☐

1452. Tony Curtis ☐

1453. No, not Edward G. Robinson; he was the kid's manager. The actor you're looking for is Wayne Morris ☐

1454. Wallace Beery, in one of his lazy slob roles ☐

1455. MacDonald Carey ☐

1456. Alan Ladd ☐

1457. Mark Stevens ☐

1458. Surely you didn't write Boris Karloff? He was the monster, Colin Clive its creator ☐

1459. Joe E. Brown ☐

1460. George Arliss, then in his sixties and a big hit with the American public ☐

The British Are Coming!

1461-2. Best original screenplay; Muriel and Sydney Box (the name Box gets you the point) ☐ ☐

1463-4. Best actor; Robert Donat ☐ ☐

1465-6. Best cinematography; Robert Krasker ☐ ☐

1467-8. Best original story; Emeric Pressburger ☐ ☐

1469-6. Best cinematography; Freddie Francis ☐ ☐

1471-2. Best original screenplay; T. E. B. Clarke ☐ ☐

1473-4. Best original screenplay; Paul Dehn, James Bernard (Frank Harvey and Roy Boulting also contributed; any one of the four names gets you the point) ☐ ☐

1475-6. Best written screenplay; George Bernard Shaw ☐ ☐

1477-8. Best actress; Simone Signoret *or* Best screenplay adapted from another medium; Neil Paterson ☐ ☐

1479–80. Best supporting actress; Margaret Rutherford □ □

Transvestites

1481–4. Elisabeth Bergner: Katharine Hepburn: Veronica Lake: Annabella □ □ □ □

1465–6. *Homicidal*: William Castle □ □

1467. *Charley's Aunt* □

1488–9. *Where's Charley?* Ray Bolger □ □

1490. Charlie Chaplin □

1491. Laurel and Hardy □

1492. Harry Ritz of the Ritz Brothers □

1493–4. Jimmy Durante: *You're in the Army Now* □ □

1495–6. Chico and Harpo Marx: *A Night at the Opera* □ □

1497–9. Cary Grant: *Bringing Up Baby*. He said, 'I just went gay all of a sudden,' and that may be the first use of the word 'gay' in something like its modern meaning □ □ □

1500. *The Devil Doll* □

1501. *The Unholy Three* □

1502. Alastair Sim □

1503–5. Arthur Treacher, Walter Catlett, Sterling Holloway □ □ □

1506. For his own good reasons Whale had her play the aged patriarch of the Femm family, complete with straggly white beard. She was listed as John Dudgeon □

1507–10. Renate Muller, *Viktor und Viktoria* (1933); Jessie Matthews, *First a Girl* (1935) □ □ □ □

1490. *National Velvet* (1944). She disguised herself as a boy jockey □

1512. *The Black Sheep of Whitehall*:□

1513. Boris Karloff □

1514. Mickey Rooney □

1515. *Knight Without Armour*: Robert Donat □

1516. Tim Curry □

1517. *The Shakiest Gun in the West* □

1518. Jane Russell ☐

1519. Calamity Jane ☐

1520. Elisabeth Bergner ☐

D–I–S–A–S–T–E–R–S

1521. *The Sisters* (1938) ☐

1522. *Fate is the Hunter* (1964) ☐

1523. *Forever Amber* (1967) ☐

1524. Locusts ☐

1525. A coal mine disaster ☐

1526. Because atomic tests knocked the earth off its axis and sent it reeling towards the sun ☐

1527. *Morning Departure* (1951) ☐

1528. An erupting volcano ☐

1529. George Pal ☐

1530. *The Poseidon Adventure* ☐

1531. *The Greatest Show on Earth* (1953) ☐

1532. Jack Holt ☐

1533. *The Rains of Ranchipur* ☐

1534. Jon Hall ☐

1535. *Intolerance* (1916) ☐

1536. *Airport* (1969) ☐

1537. *A Night to Remember* (1958) (starring Kenneth More) ☐

1538. A forest fire ☐

1539. *The Man Who Could Work Miracles* (1935) ☐

1540. Nero (in *The Story of Mankind, Quo Vadis?* and *The Sign of the Cross* respectively) ☐

Graduation Paper

1541. Lou Jacobi ☐

1542. Dana Andrews ☐

1543–6. *The Finest Hours* and *Painting as a Pastime* (for Churchill);

A King's Story (for the Duke); *The Valiant Years* (television series) ☐ ☐ ☐ ☐

1547. *Brats* ☐

1548–50. *To Have and Have Not*; Ernest Hemingway; Audie Murphy ☐ ☐ ☐

1551. Claudette Colbert ☐

1552. Frank Buck ☐

1553. George Zucco ☐

1554. *Footsteps in the Fog* ☐

1555–6. Virginia Bruce; Colin Clive ☐ ☐

1557. *The Last of Sheila* ☐

1558. *Devotion* (it purported to tell the story of the Brontës) ☐

1559–62. Simone Signoret, Vera Clouzot, Paul Meurisse; *The Fiends* or *Diabolique* or *Les Diaboliques* ☐ ☐ ☐ ☐

1563–5. Carol Foreman; Carol Reed; Sophia Loren ☐ ☐ ☐

1566–9. Deborah Kerr; Ginger Rogers; Dennis Morgan; *Too Dangerous to Love* ☐ ☐ ☐ ☐

1570. *Perfect Understanding* ☐

1571–3. Jessie Ralph; Lennox Pawle; Hugh Walpole, who was being courted by MGM to write scripts ☐ ☐ ☐

1574–5. *The Light That Failed*; Ida Lupino ☐ ☐

1576–8. *The Extraordinary Seaman*; John Frankenheimer; Faye Dunaway ☐ ☐ ☐

1579–81. James Stephenson; Herbert Marshall; Cecil Kellaway ☐ ☐ ☐

1582. Edward Ellis – not William Powell. The 'thin man' was the murder victim ☐

1583–4. Thomas Mitchell; Edna Best ☐ ☐

1585. The American desert ☐

1586–7. Orson Welles; Victor Mature ☐ ☐

1588–91. Rock Hudson; Dorothy Malone; Robert Stack; *The Tarnished Angels*. It didn't jell ☐ ☐ ☐ ☐

1592. Jane Darwell ☐

1593–6. He played it himself, a dual role. Halliwell Hobbes. Mr Hyde in *Dr Jekyll and Mr Hyde* (Fredric March version) ☐ ☐ ☐ ☐

1597. False. It was René Clair ☐

1598. *Just a Gigolo* ☐

1599–1600. Robinson Crusoe and Man Friday (in *Man Friday*) ☐ ☐

1601. *Rocco and His Brothers* ☐

1602–5. *Robinson Crusoeland*; *Atoll K*; Stan Laurel and Oliver Hardy ☐ ☐ ☐ ☐

1606. *The Miracle of Morgan's Creek* ☐

1607–8. *Escape in the Desert*; Helmut Dantine ☐ ☐

1609–10. Edward G. Robinson; Vilma Banky ☐ ☐

1611. Kay Kyser ☐

1612–13. *The Scarface Mob*; Neville Brand ☐ ☐

1614. *Forever Darling* ☐

1615–16. *Force of Evil*; John Garfield ☐ ☐

1617–19. Leslie Banks; Robert Newton; William Walton ☐ ☐ ☐

1620. Rosalind Russell ☐

1621–2. Maria Casares; through a mirror ☐ ☐

1623. *The Monte Carlo Story* ☐

1624–5. A gorilla; Eugene Pallette ☐ ☐

1626. *The Exterminating Angel* ☐

1627. *Don't Knock the Rock* ☐

1628. *Demetrius and the Gladiators* ☐

1629. *Kind Hearts and Coronets* ☐

1630–33. Maurice Chevalier; Don Ameche; *Folies Bergere*; *That Night in Rio* ☐ ☐ ☐ ☐

1634–6. Charles Laughton; Claudette Colbert; Wilson Barrett ☐ ☐ ☐

1637–8. *The Revenge of Frankenstein*; Michael Gwynn ☐ ☐

1639–40. *The Howards of Virginia*; *The Tree of Liberty* ☐ ☐

Score Sheet

score

Orientation Quiz	_____/100
Mr Laurel And Mr Hardy	_____/20
All Creatures Great And Small	_____/10
Mind Your Ps, Never Mind The Qs	_____/10
Early Days	_____/10
Slight Seconds	_____/20
They're Either Too Young Or Too Old	_____/20
Yanks At Oxford (and elsewhere)	_____/10
Were There No British Gels Available?	_____/10
Actors Should Be Treated Like ... Gold Dust	_____/10
People Of Character	_____/10
Actors We Like	_____/10
Not So Leading Ladies	_____/20
When They Were Bad They Were Horrid	_____/20
What's In A Name?	_____/20
Same Difference	_____/10
State Of The Union	_____/10
Occupational Hazards	_____/10
The Not-So-Swinging Seventies	_____/10
What's My Line?	_____/10
Mixed Doubles	_____/30
Dignity, Always Dignity	_____/30
World Gazetteer	_____/10
Sleuths	_____/10
A Rose By Any Other Name	_____/10
The Bad And The Ugly	_____/10
There's Always A First Time	_____/10

Modern Types	_____/10
The Previous Time Around	_____/40
Run For Your Life	_____/10
Hollywood At War	_____/50
It Must Stand For Something	_____/10
City Streets	_____/10
Catchphrase	_____/10
One-Shots	_____/10
One-Two Shots	_____/10
Laurence Olivier	_____/10
Very Important People	_____/20
Graham Greenery	_____/10
Hey, Mister!	_____/10
Brush Up Your Shakespeare	_____/10
Frank Capra's People	_____/30
Cherchez La Femme	_____/20
Cherchez L'Homme	_____/10
A.K.A.	_____/20
Sing As We Go	_____/80
City Of My Dreams	_____/10
My Story	_____/20
The Haunted House Of Hammer	_____/20
The Hammer Ladies	_____/10
Black-Hearted Men	_____/40
It Happened This Way	_____/10
Not All My Own Work	_____/10
Name And Address	_____/10
Pictorial Quiz: Find The Title	_____/70
Split Personalities	_____/20

Who Wrote The Book?	_____/20
Author! Author!	_____/20
Include Me Out	_____/10
Creature Features	_____/10
The Common Touch	_____/20
Sherlock Holmes	_____/10
Tinseltown	_____/10
Best Actors	_____/50
Best Actresses	_____/60
Colourful Titles	_____/10
Strength Of Character	_____/10
Crystal Balls	_____/10
Dickens	_____/20
My Life In Print	_____/20
My Life In Pictures	_____/10
States Of The Union	_____/10
It Takes Two To Tango	_____/20
Hour Of Glory	_____/20
Keep It In The Family	_____/10
Step Into My Shoes	_____/20
Forever Ealing	_____/10
Titled Ladies	_____/10
Titled Gents	_____/10
The British Are Coming!	_____/20
Transvestites	_____/40
D-I-S-A-S-T-E-R-S	_____/20
Graduation Paper	_____/100

Total Score _____/1640